CONTENTS

MY GIANT FAIRYTALE BOOK

INTRODUCTION

Here is a book full of happy and beautiful things —
chosen specially for you!

We have had a wonderful time looking through
some of the books which we have published over
the years to make this special selection for you.
Wondering and deciding whether to include this
story and that rhyme has been great fun, and we
hope and indeed feel sure that you will agree with
our final selection. You will be fascinated by the
story of the competition held among the birds to
discover who among them was fit to be their king.
You will be enchanted by the tale of the little blue
flower who became a birthday gift for the Christ
Child, and did you know that some people in the
nursery rhymes really did exist?

Here then is your own special book — have hours
of fun reading it!

OLD MOTHER HUBBARD

THE STORY OF THE NURSERY RHYME

"Rover, have you been having your friends to a party again?" asked Mother Hubbard, as she surveyed her empty cupboard. "I stocked up my shelves before going to visit my friend Dame Dob, and now there isn't a morsel of food left."

Her little dog had the grace to look very ashamed of himself as he answered humbly: "Yes, I invited Cob and Chitterabob, and the three blind mice. You know how the King likes all the animals in Nursery Rhyme Land to be good friends," he added, slyly. "I always try and please His Majesty, whenever I can."

"You sly old dog," laughed Mother Hubbard, who was really very fond of Rover. "Now I suppose I shall have to try and reach the shops before they close. And although you have had a party this afternoon I suppose you will still want something else to eat?"

"Yes, please, Mistress," said Rover, eagerly. "Actually, what I really fancy is a nice dish of tripe."

"Do you, indeed!" cried Mother Hubbard, as she picked up her shopping basket. "Other dogs make do with bones. Well, I will see what I can find, but don't get into any more mischief while I am away," she warned.

"Mischief, Mistress?" said Rover, looking at Mother Hubbard with his big, brown, innocent eyes. "When do I ever get into mischief?"

"Almost every day," replied Mother Hubbard, with a twinkle in her bright green eyes. "I still remember the day I went down to the greengrocer's shop to buy some oranges, and when I came back, there you were piping away merrily on Tom, the piper's son's magic pipes, making everyone dance, whether they liked it or not!"

"But everyone really enjoyed themselves," Rover defended himself. "Why, even Dame Dob danced with Crispin, the crooked man. They told me afterwards that my piping had made them both feel quite young again."

"Hmm, but the next day they were both full of aches and pains," replied Mother Hubbard. "Now remember, Rover, if you are naughty you will get no tripe for your supper. Oh, while I am out shopping I may as well take my shoes to the cobbler to be repaired."

Mother Hubbard went out, and Rover settled himself down in a comfortable armchair to await her return. "I might as well read the latest news about what is going on in Nursery Rhyme Land," he said.

He picked up a paper and began to read it aloud. "The Three Wise Men of Gotham have put to sea again in a bowl. I wonder why they don't use a ship? I'm sure they would find it much more comfortable. And who is this fine fellow?" he murmured, as he caught sight of a picture of a handsome young cat, in a fine, satin coat, brightly-plumed hat and matching leather boots. "Why, it is Puss in Boots, paying a visit to Nursery Rhyme Land to see his friend Chitterabob, the cat who lives with Dob and Mob."

Although Rover continued to read the newspaper, he found himself continually turning back to the page with the picture of Puss in Boots.

"He really does look a fine cat," he said at last. "And I do not see why only cats should wear smart clothes. When my mistress returns I shall ask her if I, too, may have a fine suit of clothes."

9

Suddenly Rover realised that he was sitting on something hard and was beginning to feel very uncomfortable. He searched behind him with his paw and found himself grasping a fine old carved pipe. "Why, it's Crispin the crooked man's best pipe," cried Rover. "He must have left it behind the last time he came to visit my mistress."

At that moment Rover heard Mother Hubbard returning and, with a wicked little chuckle, he put the pipe in his mouth.

"Rover, surely you are not smoking?" gasped the old lady in horror. "You promised me that you would be good."

"And I have been," replied Rover. "See, the pipe is empty. I found it just this minute, down the side of the arm-chair. Crispin will be pleased to get it back, won't he?"

"Yes, indeed," said Mother Hubbard, looking very pleased. "I see that you deserve your tripe, Rover. Here it is, a pound of the best honeycomb. I hope you enjoy it."

She watched fondly as Rover began his meal, and then she settled down to look at the paper.

"Have you seen the picture in the paper of Puss in Boots?" asked Rover, as he swallowed the last morsel of tripe.

"Yes, I think he looks very smart," smiled the old lady. "Fine feathers make fine birds."

"And don't you think that fine clothes would make a smart dog?" urged Rover, eagerly. "Oh, Mother Hubbard, can I have a suit of clothes just like that?"

"Dear me, what a strange request," said Mother Hubbard, looking at her pet in bewilderment. Then she smiled, and added, "But I don't see why not, Rover. Tomorrow we will go shopping and see if we can find anything suitable for you to wear."

"Thank you, Mother Hubbard," cried Rover. With a contented little sigh he lay down in front of the fire and promptly fell fast asleep.

Next day, Mother Hubbard and Rover set off to buy him some clothes.

"We will go to the cobbler's first to collect my shoes," said Mother Hubbard.

Cobb the cobbler was very surprised when Rover asked to try on a new pair of shoes, but he found him a lovely pair with silver buckles.

"They feel rather uncomfortable," admitted Rover, as he walked out of the shop. "But I suppose I must be prepared to suffer a little in order to be smart," he said to Mother Hubbard, who hid her little smile.

Mother Hubbard left Rover outside

the tailor's shop while she went inside to buy him a coat and some trousers. As Mr. Needlebright was wrapping up a green velvet suit, with a matching hat with a crimson feather, he and Mother Hubbard noticed that Pincushion, the tailor's young apprentice, was gazing out of the window with a huge grin on his face.

"Get on with your work, boy," ordered Mr. Needlebright crossly. "Why are you staring out of the window?"

"'Tis Mistress Hubbard's dog," laughed the boy. "He is riding the goat belonging to the Welsh gentleman, Johnny Morgan," he added by way of explanation. "Everyone is cheering and applauding the way Rover is staying on the goat's back. It really is a comical sight."

"Is it, indeed!" cried Mother Hubbard, as she seized her parcel and rushed out of the shop.

"Rover, get down from that animal's back at once," she said sternly.

One look at his mistress's face showed Rover that Mother Hubbard was very cross, so, tossing the reins back to Mr. Morgan, he jumped off and hurried over to her.

"I really am sorry, Mother Hubbard, I was only trying to hold the goat for Johnny while he sold his pigs' tails," he said, with a penitent smile.

"You don't deserve to be the best dressed dog in Nursery Rhyme Land," said Mother Hubbard, sternly wagging her finger at Rover. "However, it seems a pity to waste the clothes, especially since I have a fine shirt to go

with them from Mistress Linen the seamstress."

"Ah, yes, I remember going to buy that shirt," thought Rover to himself, with a little secret smile. "It was the day I tried to use Mistress Linen's spinning wheel and pricked my paw badly on the spindle. Goodness, it *did* hurt."

But he decided not to mention the visit to Mother Hubbard as they walked home together . . . because that would be just something else which showed that he was always up to some mischief.

But all thoughts of past pranks vanished as Rover gazed at himself in the mirror, when he had put on all his new clothes.

"You look a real gentleman, indeed you do!" cried Mother Hubbard, who had herself put on a new gown. "Come, Rover, let's away and see Dame Trot and her cat, so that all Nursery Rhyme Land can see our new finery."

"Willingly, mistress," cried Rover, with a gallant bow, "for I am sure that everyone will say that we are the most elegant couple in the land."

And of course, everyone did!

RHYMES ROUND THE YEAR

The north wind doth blow,
And we shall have snow,
And what will the robin do then, poor thing?
He'll sit in a barn
And keep himself warm,
And hide his head under his wing, poor thing.

The cuckoo comes in April,
Stops all the month of May,
Sings a song at midsummer,
And then he goes away.

Harvest home,
Harvest home,
Never a load
Has been overthrown.

Butterfly, butterfly,
Whence do you come?
I know not, I ask not,
I never had a home.
Butterfly, butterfly,
Where do you go?
Where the summer sun shines,
And where the buds grow.

One misty moisty morning, when cloudy was the weather,
There I met an old man clothed all in leather;
Clothed all in leather, with a cap under his chin,
"How do you do, and how do you do, and how do you do again!"

A swarm of bees in May
Is worth a load of hay;
A swarm of bees in June
Is worth a silver spoon;
A swarm of bees in July
Is not worth a fly.

Summer breeze, so softly blowing,
In my garden pinks are growing
If you go and send the showers,
You may come and smell my flowers.

The fair maid who, on the first of May,
Goes to the fields at break of day,
And washes in dew from the hawthorn tree
Will ever after handsome be.

A silver cup with a name upon it,
A china doll with muff and bonnet;
A grey felt cat with pretty kittens;
A rabbit cape and scarlet mittens,
All these are on the Christmas tree
As lovely gifts for baby and me.

THE FRIENDLIEST TOAD

"Ha-ha-ha, ho-ho-ho, he-he-he!"

There were such sounds of merriment coming from Woodpecker's tree-trunk house. Toad, sitting on a lily-pad in the middle of the pond, felt even more unhappy. He longed to join in the fun – BUT – he was TOO SHY!

A tear rolled down his cheek and plopped into the water. Before anyone could see him crying, Toad swam quickly away and hid amongst the rushes. Poor Toad!

Soon his tears stopped and peering through the rushes Toad saw a notice nailed to the big oak tree. He jumped out of the pond and hopped up to look. It read:—

ANYONE BRINGING THE WIZARD OF HAPPY TOWN BACK FROM CHUBBY TOWN WILL BE GRANTED A WISH

The King of Happy Town

"Whatever could be the matter in Happy Town?" thought Toad. What indeed!

The King of Happy Town, thinking that all his subjects were looking sad instead of happy, had decided something must be done about it. His Wizard was away visiting his brother in Chubby Town, so he could not help.

"If I read the Book of Spells," thought the King, "I shall be able to make everyone smile again!"

He picked up the Wizard's magic stick and thumbed through the Book of Spells. But the spell must have gone wrong somewhere because, instead of all his subjects smiling again, they all began to cry!

What an upset there was! The baker burnt his buns, the butcher chopped his fingers, the grocer dropped the butter, while the fishmonger, poor man, slipped and fell head first into the waste bin!

Toad was quite excited to read the end of the notice – A WISH! This was his chance to lose his shyness. Before he could change his mind he packed a 'kerchief and set off.

He crossed the bridge over the pond and wondered which way to go. Being too shy to ask anyone he hopped off towards the river. On the riverbank he saw Rat curled up in a hollow tree trunk.

"I really must ask if I am going the right way," thought Toad to himself. He plucked up his courage and opened his mouth to ask Rat but – nothing happened! Toad was so upset he hopped into the river and swam to the other bank before Rat opened his eyes.

Here he found himself amongst waving corn so high it might as well have been a forest.

"It is no use," sighed Toad, "I will have to go back and ask Rat."

Something moved ahead of him and, peering through the corn, he saw that it was Mouse. Plucking up every ounce of his courage this time he called, "Which way is it to Chubby Town, Mouse, please?" His voice sounded rather squeaky but Mouse looked up. When he saw that it was Toad he was so surprised he twitched his whiskers thoughtfully before replying, "Over the river and up the path through the woods to the meadow."

He had been going the wrong way all the time!

Back he went over the river and up the path to the woods. It was rather dark when he reached the trees so Toad hopped along quickly wishing he was out in the sunshine again.

Suddenly there was such a rustling and fluttering in the bushes! His heart beating fast, he forced himself along the path. Then it happened! A black form hurled itself towards him! Toad closed his eyes with fright and then when nothing hit him peeped through his eyelids and saw – BLACKBIRD!

"Oh, Blackbird, you gave me such a shock," he said breathlessly.

"Sorry," said Blackbird and flew off through the trees.

After this Toad went at full speed through the woods and soon he saw the sun shining in front of him. There was the meadow and sitting in a hollow sunning himself was Rabbit. Toad hopped over to him.

"Which way is it to Chubby Town, Rabbit, please?"

Rabbit was so surprised to hear Toad speaking to him that he waggled his ears thoughtfully before replying, "Over the meadow and up the mountain."

Toad hopped off over the meadow and up the mountain path. He huffed and he puffed but he did not stop until he reached the top. Goat was there busily chewing grass.

"Which way is it to Chubby Town, Goat, please?"

Goat was so surprised to hear Toad speaking to him that he actually stopped chewing for a moment before replying, "Down the mountain path and over the bridge."

It was much easier hopping down the mountain and Toad was soon on the bridge leading into Chubby Town. He followed the sign-post to the Palace in too much of a hurry to notice that all the people here were small and fat! Everyone turned as Toad rushed past them and watched him pull the Palace bell-rope.

The footman took him up to the Palace attics where the Wizard of Happy Town and his brother, the Wizard of Chubby Town, were making spells together.

When he saw the two great Wizards, Toad tried to hide behind the footman! However, he was much too big and the Wizard of Chubby Town asked what he wanted. Toad began to explain.

"Speak up, my good fellow, no one is going to eat you," laughed the Wizard.

His heart beating fast, Toad raised his voice and told the Wizards all about the King of Happy Town and his subjects.

"Goodness gracious!" gasped the Wizard of Happy Town. "I must get back at once."

Saying goodbye to his brother, he told Toad to stand next to him and close his eyes. The Wizard of Chubby Town drew a circle round them with his magic stick.

"HOTCH, POTCH, PITCH and DOWN, TAKE US BACK TO HAPPY TOWN," chanted the Wizard of Happy Town.

In a flash they were standing on the Palace steps. The King and Queen were there, tears streaming down their cheeks. Toad was so surprised to be back that he forgot himself and offered the Queen his clean handkerchief. The King handed the magic stick to the Wizard, begging him to hurry and make them all smile again.

"FIZZLE, WIZZLE, COUNT TO TEN, MAKE THE PEOPLE SMILE AGAIN," chanted the Wizard quickly.

Immediately everyone began to smile and feel happy again.

"Three cheers for the Wizard," they shouted.

"Three cheers for Toad for bringing him," shouted the King. "Now, Toad, let us hear your wish."

When the Wizard heard Toad's wish he laughed and said, "Why, Toad, you lost your shyness on your journey to Chubby Town!"

Toad thought about it and found he did not feel the least bit shy any more!

"Now you can have another wish," smiled the King.

"That was my only one," replied Toad.

"Well then, let me think," said the King. "How would you like to be my Chief Footman here at the Palace?"

Toad was delighted, of course!

He wears his splendid uniform proudly and while keeping his dignity as befits a Royal Chief Footman, he is known as the friendliest Toad in Happy Town.

Fairy Welcome's washing day

Little Fairy Welcome likes anything which begins with the letter W. Look carefully at the picture and see how many objects you can see beginning with the letter W. There are twelve altogether.

1. Wings 2. Wand 3. Washing 4. Willow tree. 5. Wash tub. 6. Web. 7. Witch. 8. Wood. 9. Wall. 10. Wallflowers. 11. Well. 12. Windmill.

Lennie Lamp-post had stood for nearly a hundred years in School Street, and had watched little boys and girls grow into parents, grandparents and even great-grandparents, and their children play around him in the lamplight, and swing on his strong arm—and sometimes break his windows.

He was a gas-lit lamp, and away up the street, two hundred yards away, was another lamp, like himself, whom he called Twinkle. Long ago he and Twinkle had learned to signal to each other when anything of interest was happening. But they had never been near enough in all the hundred years to talk together, since the day when they were brought to the street on the same cart.

One day, workmen came and erected a tall electric standard lamp a few yards from Lennie the Lamp-post. Lennie called him the Giant, because he towered high above the houses and could see over the railway, beyond the canal, to the green countryside that Lennie had only heard about from the children back from holidays.

Soon they became great friends. The Giant would tell Lennie of the happenings he could see, miles away, and Lennie would tell him of the happenings of long ago, and about the famous people who had once played around him, when they were children.

Lennie the Lamp Post

One Monday morning, workmen came with a cart, and dug up poor Twinkle. As he was carted past Lennie, he called, "Goodbye, Lennie. I am going to the scrap yard. I hope they may let you stay . . ."

Lennie was very upset; and he didn't feel much better when the Giant said, "Well, perhaps they will melt you down and make you into something quite different . . ."

"I shan't know how to *do* anything different," Lennie replied.

That evening a man came walking slowly up the street. He stood beneath Lennie the Lamp-post and rested his hand on him for a while, and felt a scar that Lennie had forgotten was there. Then he sat on the school wall and looked up at the light. Tonight there were no children playing around him, and Lennie knew—because the cats and dogs had told him—they would all be watching television.

Lennie thought he had seen the man before—but a long time ago, and he couldn't quite remember him. He shone his light all the brighter, until it lit up the bronzed skin of the man's face, his keen blue eyes and greying hair. At last the man tapped out his pipe and went away.

For the next week Lennie looked for the men with the cart, and then, at last, they came.

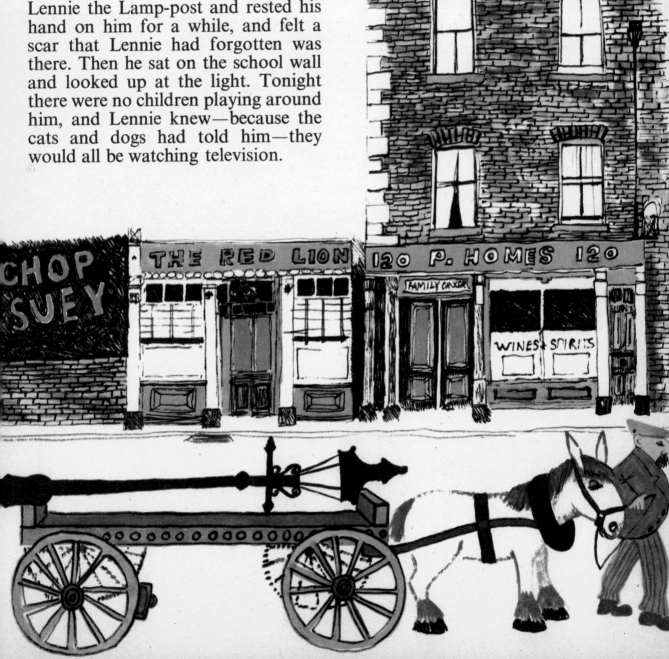

"I shall be sorry to lose you," said the Giant, "and no children will play around *me*. But I can see a long way over the railway, across the canal and away into the countryside, so I shall not be lonely."

For the first time in a hundred years Lennie the Lamp-post lay down. The cart bumped down the street and away down the road to the scrap yard. And there Twinkle lay awaiting him.

"I am sorry they have taken you up," said Twinkle, "but, oh, I am so glad to see you again, my friend."

For nearly a week they lay there and then, one day, a lorry drew up beside them. Men unloaded four packing cases; two long, narrow ones, and two square ones, with holes in. Into the cases they packed Lennie and

Twinkle and presently drove them away, out of the scrap yard, to the station.

Neither of them had seen a train before, though they had heard them whistle. They didn't much like being loaded into a truck, and when the train began to move, they huddled together, *bumpety-bump, bumpety-bump,* until at last they felt safe. They passed through the city, and across the canal.

"Look, there's the Giant," cried Lennie to Twinkle.

"I can't see," said Twinkle.

"Yes, you can," called Lennie, "there are holes on the other side of your box."

As they passed through the countryside they saw for the first time the green grass, trees, cornfields, people

making hay. Once they crossed a broad river, and beside it stood lamp-posts like themselves, their light glinting on the water. They went past brickworks, through orchards, past a lake with boats bobbing, past factories and flour mills, and poultry farms and foundries, until they came, at last, to the sea.

The men dumped them, side by side, on the dock. They watched the water going away, and were surprised when it came back again in the evening.

"I wish it would make up its mind," said Twinkle, "whether it wants to stay or not. I do believe it's going back again . . ."

A crane lifted them on board a ship, and there they formed part of the deck cargo. When the morning tide was high, the ship weighed anchor and sailed out of the docks, down to the sea.

"Why," said Lennie, "the land is moving away. Where on earth is it going? I don't think I like this, Twinkle."

Twinkle was quite sure *he* didn't. Further and further the land receded, until at last they could see it no more. Only, as night fell, they could see a light flashing sometimes, for a few seconds—and then, at last, in the grey dawn, even that disappeared.

For a long time after that they saw nothing but sea. Huge rolling waves on windy days, and smooth glassy sea on calm days. If it hadn't been for the sailors, talking and singing, it would have been a monotonous journey.

Through the holes of their cases, Lennie and Twinkle could see other ships far off, with hundreds of lights at night, and gay white paint in the daytime. There were fat, tubby little cargo boats, and oil tankers, and ocean-going yachts, and sometimes a big fishing trawler. But when they got further out to sea, and even the seagulls had been left behind, they saw only an occasional big ship, hooting as it passed, and sometimes the sailors called, "Ahoy!"

They sighted land in the third week. "Lennie, look," cried Twinkle. "What is that rising out of the sea?"

"Why, it's like a great statue," said Lennie the Lamp-post. "Wherever can we be?"

"It's not the land that went away before," said Twinkle. "It's some more land."

Once again great cranes lifted them ashore, this time onto a huge truck, which set off with them at once. Through strange streets they travelled, with giant buildings on either side.

"Why," said Lennie, "even the Giant would be tiny here. He couldn't reach anywhere near the tops of these."

"I think they must be skyscrapers," said Twinkle, thoughtfully. "I've heard the schoolchildren talk about them."

26

"Everybody looks very different here," said Lennie. "And they talk like the children do when they're playing gangsters and cowboys. Yes, I think our country has drifted away and America has come."

It never occurred to them that the ship had moved!

The truck driver drove carefully, so as not to break the glass. He drove a long way, and again, when they were out of the city, they saw strange things. There were white wooden houses, and strange-looking cars, and sometimes a horse and buggy and, at last, a frightening locomotive with a huge fender on the front.

"Are things ever going to stop moving?" asked Twinkle.

"I hope not," replied Lennie. "After a hundred years in one place it's time we saw something."

And they settled down to enjoy themselves.

But at last their journey was done.

The train stopped in the middle of the plain, "a hundred miles from nowhere," as Lennie said. There was a tiny platform and shed, and here they were unloaded and put onto a farm cart.

"Careful, Sam," said the driver, as the coloured porter helped him load them. "These have come all the way

from England, and if we break 'em I sure don't know what Mr. Jackson will say."

That night they lay in a farmyard, with hens scratching around them and perching. Dogs sniffed curiously, cats explored the packing cases and a strange bird circled above.

Then the strange man whom Lennie had seen just before he was moved came to inspect them. "I can't bear to leave them till morning," he said to his farm hand. "Let's open them up."

"Sure, boss," said the man and, fetching a case opener, he soon had the lids off.

The strange man looked down at them, beaming. "I've got everything fixed for you two," he declared. "Just wait till morning. Cover them up carefully, Bud."

"I think we've come to the end of our journey," declared Lennie. "I do believe we're going to stay here."

"What would they want with us on a ranch out on the plain?" wondered Twinkle. "It's all very strange . . ."

But next evening they were both standing erect in the courtyard of the huge white house beyond the ranch. One on either side of the gateway they stood, their glasses polished till they shone, and a bright

28

electric light throwing cheerful beams away into the night and over a group of children who played beneath.

The man who had tapped out his pipe on the lamp-post stood once more beneath Lennie. He fingered the dent made by the axe wielded by a small boy a long time ago, and he said: "This is the street lamp I told you about. And this is the dent I made when I was ten, long before I came to America."

"Whatever for, Grandad?" asked one of the children, swarming up Twinkle.

"Well, you see," said his grandfather, "I so wanted to live in the country that I pretended the lamp was a tree."

The children laughed and danced around in a circle.

"And when I came out here, I missed the lamplight at night and couldn't go to sleep. I knew that far away across the sea the lamps would still be lit each night—and I made up my mind that when I was able, I would bring this particular lamp to my home—and here he is, with his brother from away up the street."

"Lennie the Lamp-post," cried one of the children.

"And Twinkle," cried another.

"We'll never try to chop you down," declared the third.

"And we'll never break your windows," promised the fourth.

"It's bedtime," said their grandfather. "Come. In your bedrooms you can see the lamplight. It will be there all the night, if you awake . . ."

Lennie thought back a long, long way. Forty years, fifty years . . . . . And he *did* remember the small boy who had tried to chop him down, so long ago . . . . . .

SIX
SLEEPYHEADS

Elsie Marley is grown so fine,
She won't get up to feed the swine,
But lies in bed till eight or nine.
Lazy Elsie Marley.

Diddle, diddle, dumpling, my son John,
Went to bed with his trousers on;
One shoe off, and one shoe on,
Diddle, diddle, dumpling, my son John.

Wee Willie Winkie runs through the town,
Upstairs and downstairs in his nightgown,
Rapping at the windows, crying through the lock,
"Are the children all in bed, for now it's eight o'clock."

Robin and Richard
Were two pretty men,
They lay in bed
Till the clock struck ten,
Then up starts Robin
And looks at the sky,
"Oh, Brother Richard,
The sun's very high.
You go before
With the bottle and bag,
And I will come after
On little Jack Nag."

"Lazy Mary, will you get up,
Will you get up, will you get up,
Lazy Mary, will you get up,
Will you get up today?"
"No, no, Mother, I won't get up,
I won't get up, I won't get up,
No, no, Mother, I won't get up,
I won't get up today."

"Come, let's to bed,"
Cried Sleepyhead.
"Nay, tarry awhile,"
Said Slow.
"Put on the pan,"
Cried greedy Nan,
"We'll sup before we go."

King
of the

MANY years ago, the raven was king of all the birds. He was not a good king and all the other birds feared and disliked him.

They would have liked to have chosen another king and put the raven off the throne. But every time they planned to do this, somehow or other the raven got word of it. He would challenge the bird who wanted to be king to fight a duel with him. Of course none of the birds would fight, for they all knew how strong and fierce the raven was, and how hopeless the contest would be.

The truth was, that if the magpie decided *he* would like to be king, the wood-pigeon went to the raven and told him what was going on. If the jackdaw wanted to be king, the magpie would again inform the raven.

After a time the raven became tired of all this trouble in his kingdom, so he summoned all his subjects to a court meeting.

All the birds went to the meeting, for they were afraid of the punishment that was always in store for them if they refused to obey the king's orders. Besides they were all very curious as to the meaning of this special meeting.

There were many thousands of birds, therefore, gathered round the elm tree

Birds

that morning, as the raven rose to address his subjects.

"I believe," he said, "that there are some birds among my subjects who think that they would make a better king than me."

At this all the birds looked accusingly at each other, each pretending that of course, he appreciated that the raven was the best king in the world.

"Well," continued the raven, "we will settle this matter once and for all. If there is any bird here who can fly faster than I can, *he* can be king. If there is any bird here who can see further than I can see, *he* can be king. And if there is any bird who can fly higher than I can, *he* can be king. But if no one can beat me in these contests then I must be allowed to reign in peace. Are we all agreed?"

"All in favour raise the right wing," hooted the owl, who was the wisest of all the king's councillors.

Every bird raised a wing, for the raven's proposal sounded fair enough, and anyway no one dared to vote against it.

So the owl acted as referee and all the birds entered the race, even the sparrow, who knew he couldn't fly very fast and who didn't want to be king anyway.

33

Of course the raven won the race, and all the other birds clapped politely.

Next came the contest to find out who could see the farthest. Only six birds entered this time, as the others were too tired after the race.

These six birds were the magpie, the jackdaw, the wood-pigeon, the hawk, the sparrow and, of course, the raven. Everyone laughed at the sparrow for entering the race, but the sparrow didn't care. The truth was that the sparrow hated the raven because the king had turned the whole sparrow family out of their nest because they couldn't pay their annual tax of twenty worms. The sparrow was determined that *he* would be the one to overthrow the cruel king.

So these six birds sat in a row on a branch of a tree.

" Now," said the owl, " what can you see, sparrow? "

" I can see a meadow," said the sparrow timidly.

" In that meadow I can see a farm-house," said the wood-pigeon.

" On that farmhouse I can see a window," said the magpie.

" On that window I can see a spider's web," said the jackdaw.

" On that spider's web I can see a spider," said the hawk.

The raven cocked his head on one side, and thought hard.

" The spider," he said, " has one eye open and the other eye shut."

As none of the others could see whether this were true or not, they had to admit that the raven had won again.

Now came the contest to see who could fly the highest. Again all the birds entered the competition, and away they went, higher and higher into the sky. No one noticed that the sparrow had jumped onto the raven's back just as the raven took off.

Very soon the other birds began to drop out until only the raven was left with, of course, the sparrow perched on his back.

After a while the raven began to feel a little dizzy, and knowing that the others would have given in by this time, he began to descend. Off flew the sparrow from the raven's back, and flew a few yards higher into the sky. The raven saw him flying up, but he did not know that the cunning sparrow had had a lift most of the way.

When the raven saw that the little sparrow had flown higher than he could he was ashamed to face the other birds, so he flew far away and built his nest on a high mountain.

As the sparrow did not want to be king, the birds held an election. The owl was voted king, and you may be sure he ruled wisely and well.

Once upon a time........

Once upon a time . . . this is the start of so many of our favourite fairy tales, but perhaps more suitable in this case is . . . Long, long ago, in lands over the water, there lived three people who are now very famous indeed. Two of them were brothers, their names were Jacob and Wilhelm Grimm; the other came from another country not very far away from Germany where the brothers were born; his name was Hans Christian Andersen.

THE BROTHERS GRIMM

Jacob Grimm was the eldest brother; he was born in 1785, his brother Wilhelm was born a year later. They were devoted to each other. From their birthplace in a town called Hanau, they went to university, where they studied together and both became very learned young men.

At first they were interested only in the German language, and Jacob even started to compile a German dictionary. For a short time the brothers were separated when Jacob went to work in Paris.

Jacob and Wilhelm are not really fairytale writers, but more fairytale tellers. They travelled all over Germany searching for old fables to re-tell in their books. Many hours were spent in kitchens and gardens, listening to grandmothers telling the stories that their grandmothers had told them as young children. This was then the only way that such stories could be heard, each area having its own fables, until the Brothers Grimm came along and collected all the stories together in a written form.

A lot of their stories were told to them by a very old lady who lived in a town in Germany called Kassel. She was a very good story teller; each tale she told seemed to come to life, and Jacob and Wilhelm spent hours listening to these tales and writing them down, so that they could be put into their books. Most of these tales were written by the brothers just as they were told and retold over hundreds of years. But some of the stories had got rather muddled through the years, so these tales were altered and rewritten by the brothers Grimm so that they were clearer to read.

Volume One of the tales collected by the Brothers Grimm was called *Nursery and Household Tales*, and was first printed in 1812, the second volume appearing three years later, in 1815. These stories included some of the most famous fairytales ever written, and a great many of our favourites too: *Hansel and Gretel, Rapunzel, Cinderella, The Goose-Girl, Snow-White,* and *The Frog King*.

Today, most of the stories that the Brothers Grimm collected can be found in one large volume, called *Grimm's Fairy Tales*. This book contains about two hundred and ten tales, collected from places all over Germany.

HANS CHRISTIAN ANDERSEN

The third person in our tale is the world-famous fairytale writer, Hans Christian Andersen.

On a fine April day in 1805, a boy was born to a poor cobbler and his wife, and as the tiny baby lay on its home-made bed, whilst its father read plays aloud, not a soul would have dreamt that this boy, born to poverty, was to become the fairytale writer of all time.

Hans Christian did not have a very happy home life. He was often sad, for even though his father wanted him to grow up into a clever and famous man, they were very poor, and it seemed that the cobbler's son would become just another poor villager. But there were happy times too, when little Hans sat with his father listening to him reading aloud, and when he walked by the riverside in the summertime.

In the long, cold winters the small Danish village of Odense was covered with snow, and Hans spent endless dusky afternoons and evenings with his father, pressing hot coins against the windows. This melted away Jack Frost's handiwork, leaving tiny peepholes to the glistening winter world of whirling snowflakes and icicles outside.

When he was fourteen, Hans Christian Andersen left his widowed mother and the village which had been his home to go to Copenhagen, where he hoped to become an actor. The little money that he had saved did

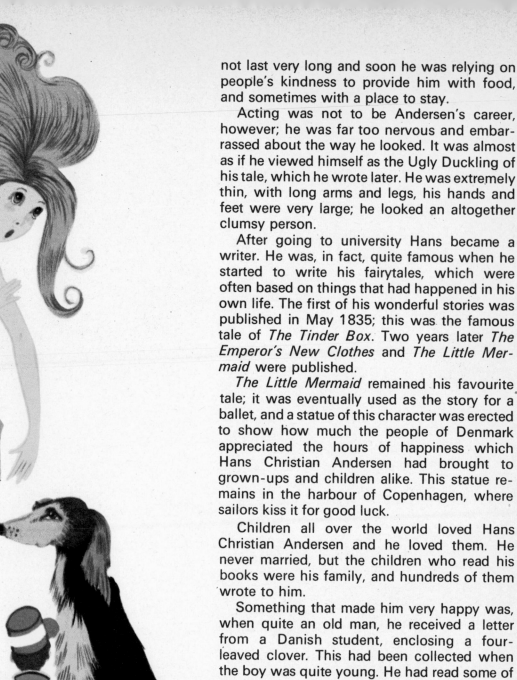

not last very long and soon he was relying on people's kindness to provide him with food, and sometimes with a place to stay.

Acting was not to be Andersen's career, however; he was far too nervous and embarrassed about the way he looked. It was almost as if he viewed himself as the Ugly Duckling of his tale, which he wrote later. He was extremely thin, with long arms and legs, his hands and feet were very large; he looked an altogether clumsy person.

After going to university Hans became a writer. He was, in fact, quite famous when he started to write his fairytales, which were often based on things that had happened in his own life. The first of his wonderful stories was published in May 1835; this was the famous tale of *The Tinder Box*. Two years later *The Emperor's New Clothes* and *The Little Mermaid* were published.

The Little Mermaid remained his favourite tale; it was eventually used as the story for a ballet, and a statue of this character was erected to show how much the people of Denmark appreciated the hours of happiness which Hans Christian Andersen had brought to grown-ups and children alike. This statue remains in the harbour of Copenhagen, where sailors kiss it for good luck.

Children all over the world loved Hans Christian Andersen and he loved them. He never married, but the children who read his books were his family, and hundreds of them wrote to him.

Something that made him very happy was, when quite an old man, he received a letter from a Danish student, enclosing a four-leaved clover. This had been collected when the boy was quite young. He had read some of the famous fairytales, and when his mother told him that Hans Chtistian Andersen had not had an easy life, the boy had gone out into the fields to search for a four-leaved clover for his mother to send to the writer to bring him luck. The token had never been sent, but when the boy's mother died he found the clover pressed between the pages of a book and he sent it to the author to show how much the fairytales had meant to him.

Altogether Hans Christian Andersen wrote over one hundred and fifty stories. Among his most famous are *The Tinder-Box, Thumbelina, The Emperor's New Clothes, The Little Mermaid, The Ugly Duckling* and *The Princess and the Pea*.

FAIRY WEDDING

The Rainbow Fairy Queen is on her way to the wedding of Fairy Moondrops to the Prince of Bluebell Glade. But she has lost her way in the enchanted forest. Can you help her find her way to the Royal Palace, where the wedding is to be held?

The Magic Door

Penny sat in her room, staring angrily at the book in front of her. "Janet . . . and . . . John . . . went for . . . a . . . walk . . . with . . . .," she read slowly. Then she slammed the book shut with a bang. "Oh bother," she said crossly. "I hate reading, it's so dull."

"How are you getting along, dear?" Mother popped her head round the door.

"I hate reading," repeated Penny, getting crosser and crosser.

"Oh dear," sighed mother. "You are a crosspatch, to be sure. Sulking isn't going to help one little bit. Remember what your teacher said? She expects you to be able to read a few pages at least by Monday. The rest of the class are way ahead of you."

I'm sorry to say that at this point Penny pulled a face, as if to say she just didn't care. Mother pretended not to notice and went on talking. "I'm sure you could do it, if you try. I'll pop back later to see how you are getting on." And she went out again, closing the door softly behind her.

40

Penny picked up the book again, but she just couldn't raise a scrap of interest. "Stupid old book," she cried crossly, and tossed it in the corner.

"Hey, watch what you're doing," called out a little voice. "That very nearly hit me."

Penny was so surprised that she walked over to the corner where a little man, dressed in a white suit, printed all over with letters of the alphabet, was sitting cross-legged in the corner, reading a book.

"Hello," said Penny, curiously. "Who are you?"

"I'm Bookworm, of course," replied the little man. "And what seems to be the trouble with you, may I ask?"

So Penny told Bookworm all about the trouble she was having with her reading. "It's all so boring," she concluded sadly.

"Ah now," said Bookworm, "if someone were to take you through the magic door, then all your troubles would be over."

"Would you take me?" asked Penny.

"I might," replied Bookworm, "and then again I might not."

"Oh, please," begged Penny. "I'm truly sorry for nearly hitting you with that book," she added.

"Ah, that's better," smiled Bookworm. "I'll take you."

"But where is this door?" asked Penny.

"Why, right here, of course," said her new friend.

He took the book he had been reading and stood it up on end. He touched it lightly with his hand, and as he did so the book seemed to grow and Penny seemed to shrink and before she knew what was happening she was standing next to her new friend in front of a large oak door. She was just tall enough to reach the handle.

"Come on through," invited Bookworm and together they opened the door and walked through.

When they passed through the door Penny blinked in astonishment. She seemed to be in another land, or rather a whole cluster of lands all on top of one another. As she walked along with Bookworm she saw fairies, elves, pixies, toys that walked and talked like you or I, in fact hundreds of different people and creatures, each more fascinating than the last.

At one point she saw a large house, in the grounds of which stood an imposing-looking motor car. Clustered around the car were three animals, all talking excitedly.

"Who are they?" she asked, for although she had recognised some of

the people she had seen so far, these creatures were new to her.

"That's Toad, with his friends, Mole and Ratty," replied Bookworm.

Penny would like to have stayed and heard more about them but Bookworm was urging her onwards.

They were passing a stream now and Penny looked down, hoping to catch a glimpse of some fish, but to her surprise she saw not only fish but a number of children laughing and playing *underneath* the water. They weren't mermaids, of that Penny was quite sure, because they had no tails and yet they swam and dived as nimbly as any fish.

"Tom and the Water Babies," said Bookworm, as if he could read the question which was already forming in her mind. "I expect Mr. Grimes is about somewhere."

"What a funny name," laughed Penny. "Who is Mr. Grimes?"

"A chimney sweep, of course," replied Bookworm. "But come along, there's lots, lots more for you to see."

After they left Tom and the Water Babies they passed by a field where two scarecrows were busy talking.

"I never knew that scarecrows could talk," said Penny.

"But they are Worzel Gummidge and Upsidaisy," replied Bookworm, as if that explained everything.

There was so much that Penny wanted to know—why, for instance, did one of the scarecrows have three legs? But Bookworm was still hurrying her on.

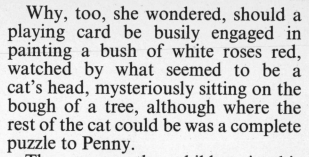

Why, too, she wondered, should a playing card be busily engaged in painting a bush of white roses red, watched by what seemed to be a cat's head, mysteriously sitting on the bough of a tree, although where the rest of the cat could be was a complete puzzle to Penny.

There were other children in this strange land. One group in particular, led by a freckle-faced boy called William, seemed to be having loads of fun.

Whichever way you turned there seemed to be something interesting, people from the past, the present and the future. Pirates and princesses, witches and dragons, people flying, people walking, people laughing, talking . . . . yes, and even crying. They all looked so interesting that Penny longed to know and find out all about them, but Bookworm never stopped long enough for her to get more than a passing glimpse, and she was afraid to stop for fear of losing her friend.

At last she was so tired out she could go no further. "Stop," she pleaded.

Bookworm looked at his watch. "Good gracious me," he cried. "I had no idea it was this late—I must take you back."

"Can't we stay?" begged Penny. "I've scarcely met these people and they all look so interesting."

"You can meet them all in books, you know," said her friend. "Every single one of them—you can read and re-read about all of them, and they will be your friends for the rest of your life."

"Read!" Suddenly Penny remembered what Bookworm had promised her: "When you pass through the magic door all your troubles will be over."

Bookworm answered her unspoken question. "Yes, your troubles are almost over," he said, "because you have found the secret."

Penny looked puzzled. "What secret?"

"Now you *want* to learn to read and that's half the battle."

Penny realised that what he had said was true. If learning to read meant meeting all these exciting people, then indeed she did want to learn, and quickly. She wanted to ask Bookworm so much more, but already the scene was fading and her friend with it.

Just then her mother came into the room to see how Penny was getting on with her reading. Penny opened the book and started to read, "Janet and—John—went—for a walk—with their—mother and father ....."

"Very good, dear," praised Mummy, when she had finished. "I knew you could do it if you tried."

"It was Bookworm who showed me the secret," whispered Penny softly .....

Now, I'm going to let you all into a little secret. Do you know that wherever you live, somewhere in that town or district there is a magic door?

I can just hear you saying, "I don't believe you," but I can assure you that it's perfectly true—there really is.

It may not be a very grand door, and probably doesn't look the least bit magical, but anyone who wishes can go through that door and find themselves in the wonderful world of books. So please, don't ever be misled into thinking that reading is something dull and boring which you have to do in school—it can open up the most wonderful world of make-believe, adventure and learning for you.

So next time you pass the door of your local public library—why not go in and borrow a book? If you are not very old I'm sure that Mummy will do it for you, and who knows what adventures will await you when you pass through the magic door?

A NURSERY RHYME SUM

How many animals are mentioned altogether in this nursery rhyme?

Three young rats
With black felt hats,
Three young ducks
With white straw flats,
Three young dogs
With curling tails,
Three young dogs
With demi-veils,
Went out to walk
With two young pigs,
In satin vests
And sorrel wigs;
But suddenly it
Chanced to rain,
And so they all
Went home again.

46

HORSES... HORSES... HORSES

There are lots of horses mentioned in familiar nursery rhymes. Do you know:—

1. What was the name of the pony who was lent to the lady who rode him through the mire?

2. Who was allowed to go bare?

3. Whose head was made from pea-straw?

4. What colour was the horse the fine lady of Banbury Cross rode?

5. Who took the foal and mare to Banbury Fair?

6. Who were asked the time of day?

7. How many horses were stuck in a bog?

8. Who could not mend Humpty Dumpty?

9. Who followed after on little Jack Nag?

10. Where was the mare lost?

11. Who came to town riding on a pony?

12. Who was the man on the black horse at Charing Cross?

You will find all the answers among the nursery rhymes on the following pages.

I had a little pony,
His name was Dapple Grey;
I lent him to a lady
To ride a mile away.
She whipped him, she slashed him,
She rode him through the mire;
I would not lend my pony now,
For all the lady's hire.

Shoe the horse,
Shoe the mare,
But let the little colt go bare, bare, bare.

I had a little hobby horse
And it was dapple grey,
Its head was made of pea-straw,
Its tail was made of hay.

I sold him to an old woman
For a copper groat,
And I'll not sing my song again
Without a new coat.

Ride a cock-horse to Banbury Cross,
To see a fine lady upon a white horse;
Rings on her fingers and bells on her toes,
She shall have music wherever she goes.

As I was going to Banbury,
Upon a summer's day,
My dame had butter, eggs, and fruit,
And I had corn and hay;
Joe drove the ox, and Tom the swine,
Dick took the foal and mare,
I sold them all — then home to dine,
From famous Banbury Fair.

Bell horses, bell horses,
What time of day?
One o'clock, two o'clock,
Time to away.

Humpty Dumpty sat on a wall,
Humpty Dumpty had a great fall;
All the king's horses, and all the king's men
Could not put Humpty Dumpty together again.

Six beetles against a wall,
Close by the apple-woman's stall,
Five puppies for our dog Ball,
Who loudly for their breakfast call,
Four horses stuck in a bog,
Three monkeys on a clog,
Two pudding pieces for a dog
And a juicy worm for a waddling frog.

Robin and Richard were two pretty men,
That lay in bed till the clock struck ten;
Then up starts Robin and looks at the sky,
"Oh, brother Richard, the sun's very high;
You go before with bottle and bag,
And I will come after on little Jack Nag."

I lost my mare in Lincoln Lane,
And couldn't tell where to find her,
Till she came home, so sad and lame,
With never a tail behind her.

Yankee Doodle came to town,
Riding on a pony;
He stuck a feather in his cap
And called it macaroni.

As I was going by Charing Cross,
I saw a black man upon a black horse;
They told me it was King Charles the Firs
Oh dear, my heart was ready to burst.

The CAT and the MOUSE

THE STORY OF
THE NURSERY RHYME

The Royal Palace was in such a whirl! The Lords and Ladies were putting on their very best clothes, and their richest jewels, and the Maids and Footmen were running in every direction. Some were carrying dainty dishes of roast chicken and ice-cream, and placing them on the long tables in the Great Hall, and some were making up all the best beds with fine linen sheets and embroidered pillowcases.

Never had there been such a fuss! Even the Royal Horses were being brushed and combed until their coats shone in the sunshine, and the Royal Coach had a fresh coat of gold paint, and plenty of oil to stop it squeaking and creaking as it rolled along.

Now all this excitement was because a beautiful Princess was coming from a faraway land to marry the King and be their new Queen!

At last she arrived in the city and as the black horses pulled her proudly through the streets in the Royal Coach all the people shouted: "Long live the Princess."

Then they reached the Palace gates and drove right up to the big front door, where the Princess stepped out of the coach and walked up the steps. She turned and waved to the people, who cheered all the more when they saw how truly beautiful she was.

The footman opened the big front door, and as the Princess entered the Palace and walked through the Great Hall, all the courtiers bowed very low, and all their ladies did a very deep curtsey.

At last she came to the Throne Room, where the King awaited her. He took her by the hand, and led her to a gold and crimson throne, and she sat down gracefully upon it.

All at once everyone was silent. Only the youngest pageboy dared to whisper to the youngest maid-of-honour that his new buckle shoes were pinching his toes, and he would much rather be in his comfortable clothes.

Then the King rose to his feet to make a royal speech of welcome to

the Princess, who was to be his Queen. But just as he was making a very low and courtly bow there was a rushing, scampering noise, and a tiny white mouse ran helter-skelter across the Throne Room, with a large tabby cat chasing after him!

Round and round the courtiers' feet, and in and out of the ladies' long dresses ran the frightened little mouse, with the pussycat slipping and sliding on the polished floor, as he drew nearer and nearer.

With a despairing squeak the little white mouse shot straight under the Royal Throne and hid beneath the hem of the Princess's white velvet gown, and all that could be seen was the quivering tip of his little pink nose.

Well, what a commotion there was, to be sure!

The Princess gave a shriek and jumped up on to the seat of the Royal Throne, holding up her long velvet gown and her six silken petticoats, and showing her dainty ankles and white satin shoes.

The King nearly tripped over on his

royal nose, as the pussycat ran between his feet and crouched in front of the throne. With his tail wagging slowly from side to side, the cat twitched his long whiskers and growled a deep sort of growl.

"Somebody remove that cat from my sight," shouted the King, in a very loud voice.

"Somebody catch the mouse," cried the Princess, in an even louder voice. "I'd much rather have cats than mice."

Immediately there was more confusion as some of the courtiers ran to catch the pussycat, and some ran to catch the mouse, and the ladies ran to the side of the room and jumped up on the little gilt chairs.

Everyone was so busy rushing around that nobody noticed the youngest pageboy give a special whistle, and the little white mouse ran quickly through all the people's feet, and up the leg of his purple hose and into the pocket of his best crimson coat.

Still nobody noticed as he slipped out of the door and ran up five flights of stairs to his tiny bedroom at the very top of the Palace. There he popped the little mouse quickly back into its cage and shut the door, and with a sigh of relief he decided he would never put his little friend in his best coat pocket again.

Back in the Throne Room the pussycat was determined that no one was going to catch him, and with a great leap he was out of the window, down the royal drive, and through the big iron gates before the courtiers could disentangle themselves and chase after him.

When he was safely back in his own home, he began to boast about his great adventure. Ever afterwards, whenever anyone came to tea, he would tell them how he upset the whole Royal Palace by chasing a little mouse under the new Queen's throne!

Nursery Rhyme Places

Can you complete the following lines in each familiar nursery rhyme with the name of a place?

As I was going to

I met a man with seven wives.

The Man in the Moon came down too soon

And asked his way to

How many miles to

Three score and ten.

Hey, diddle, dinketty, popperty, pet,

The merchants of   they wear scarlet:

The Grand Old Duke of

He had ten thousand men.

Three wise men of

Went to sea in a bowl.

Doctor Foster went to

In a shower of rain.

Ride a cock horse

To

ANSWERS

St. Ives; Norwich; Babylon; London; York; Gotham; Banbury Cross; Gloucester.

56

TINKER...TAILOR

I am sure that you all know that Bo-Peep was a shepherdess and that Boy Blue was a farmer's boy, but do you know . . .

1. What did my maid Mary do?

2. Who did the owl, the eel and the warming pan go to see?

3. Who lived by the river Dee?

4. Who was given a pinch of snuff?

5. Whose sweet songs did the birds stop to hear?

6. Whose son stole a pig?

7. Who killed a mouse within his house?

8. Who could not find anyone to marry her?

9. Who went to kill a snail?

10. Who was dressed so trim?

11. Who whistles up his team?

12. Who wear scarlet, with silk in the collar and gold in the hem?

13. Who loves his bright sword?

14. Who shouted: "Fire, fire!"

15. Who went to Gloucester?

16. Who did Simple Simon meet going to the fair?

ANSWERS

1. Minded the dairy; 2. The soap-fat man; 3. The jolly miller; 4. The barber; 5. Davy Delongs, the slim little tinker; 6. The piper's son; 7. The little priest of Felton; 8. The daughter of the farrier; 9. Four and twenty tailors; 10. Corporal Tim; 11. The carter; 12. The merchants of London; 13. The knight; 14. The town-crier; 15. Doctor Foster; 16. The pieman.

Boys and girls, come out to play,
The moon doth shine as bright as day.
Leave your supper and leave your sleep,
And join your playfellows in the street.
Come with a whoop and come with a call
Come with a good will or not at all.
Up the ladder and down the wall,
A small white loaf will serve us all;
You find milk, and I'll find flour,
And we'll have a pudding in half an hour.

Monday's child is fair of face,
Tuesday's child is full of grace,
Wednesday's child is full of woe,
Thursday's child has far to go.
Friday's child is loving and giving,
Saturday's child works hard for his living,
And the child that is born on the Sabbath day
Is bonny and blithe, and good and gay.

LITTLE BOYS AND LITTLE GIRLS

What are little girls made of?
What are little girls made of?
Sugar and spice,
And all that's nice,
That's what little girls are made of.

A little boy went into a barn,
And lay down on some hay.
An owl came out and flew about,
And the little boy ran away.

Georgie Porgie, pudding and pie,
Kissed the girls and made them cry;
When the boys came out to play,
Georgie Porgie ran away.

Little boy, little boy, where were you born?
Far away in Lancashire under a thorn,
Where they drink sour milk in a ram's horn.

"Little girl, little girl, where have you been?"
"Gathering roses to give to the queen."
"Little girl, little girl, what gave she you?"
"She gave me a diamond as big as my shoe."

There was a little girl who had a little curl
Right in the middle of her forehead;
When she was good, she was very, very good,
But when she was bad, she was horrid.

MANY years ago a little princess named Rosa lived with her father and mother, the king and queen, in a big palace surrounded by lovely gardens. Beyond was a great forest, dwarfed by high snow-capped mountains. So breathtaking was the scenery that everywhere the princess looked she could see only beauty.

The little princess was very beautiful herself. She had rosy cheeks and blue eyes, and her golden curls glittered when the sun shone upon them. But she was very, very sad.

During all her life no-one had ever heard the little princess laugh. She was always polite, and when asked if she was well she would reply, " Yes, Mama," to the queen, or " Yes, Papa," to the king, or " Yes, my Lord," to the Lord Chamberlain. When people tried to amuse her she would give them a sad little smile, but she never, never laughed.

One day the queen said to the king, " It is a great sorrow to me that our daughter is so sad. She is surrounded by everything that is beautiful and by people whose only desire is to please her, and yet she is not happy. She hardly ever plays with her toys, she does not ask to be taken for walks, and she does not seem to want anything. Could we not do something to make her enjoy life more?"

The Sad Princess

The king answered, "Dear wife, I am as anxious as you are for our daughter's happiness; but I do not know what to do."

They both thought for a minute, and then the king went on, " Our country stretches far, and within its boundaries are many people. Surely among all these people there must be one who will know how to make our daughter happy. I will have a proclamation published throughout the land that whoever can make Princess Rosa laugh, will gain a rich reward."

So the proclamation was read to the people in the towns and in the villages.

And the people said, " It is a great sorrow to us that our princess is so sad. Let us think of ways to make her happy."

From that day onwards many people came to the palace with gifts for the princess.

The first to come was an old lady who baked gingerbread to sell to the children on fair days.

"I know what all little girls like," she said, and she gave the princess a box of the most delicious candy. "Put a piece in your mouth, my dear," she urged.

The princess took a piece of candy and thanked the old lady, saying that it was very good, as indeed it was; but she did not laugh.

Next came a wise man from a neighbouring town. He said to the king and queen, " The princess is unhappy because she hasn't enough to do. Let her work in the garden among the flowers and the plants, and soon she will learn to love the beautiful things of nature, and so find true happiness."

He brought the little princess a rake, a trowel, a watering-can, and a brightly-coloured wheelbarrow. He showed her how to sow seeds, to care for the young plants, and to water them when the ground was dry. The princess liked the work in the garden and used to get up early to look after her plants; but she never laughed.

Then came a sailor boy who had just returned from across the seas. He brought the princess a small brown monkey. The monkey was sitting on his shoulder, and every now and again it would climb down his sleeve, take a peanut out of his pocket, and climb back again to eat it. The princess could not resist a smile when she saw this, and the sailor boy thought that he was going to gain the rich reward. But he was wrong, for the princess did not laugh.

At last a tall, bronzed woodcutter who lived and worked in the forest came to the palace. Close behind him, holding hands, trotted three children.

The woodman said to the king, "Your Majesty, although I live so close to the palace, I have only just heard of your proclamation, for I rarely go to the village to hear the news. A passing traveller told me that you wished someone could make the princess laugh, and so I hastened here with my children. This is my daughter, Greta, and her brothers, John and little Michael."

The children came forward, shyly but laughing, and stood before the king and queen.

The queen said, "They are fine children, woodman, and happy ones. But, tell me, what have you brought for the princess?"

The woodman looked puzzled for a minute. "Why, the children, Your Majesty," he explained. "I have brought my children to play with the princess."

The king and queen looked surprised. However they called a servant to take the children to the little princess in the garden.

A few minutes later peals of joyous laughter floated into the palace. The king and queen hurried outside, followed by the woodman, and looked to see where the laughter was coming from.

John was giving little Michael a ride in the princess's gay wheelbarrow and running behind were Greta and Princess Rosa with bunches of daisies in their hands, which they were trying to throw into the barrow. The woodman's children were laughing merrily, and when the king and queen looked at the princess, they saw that *she* was laughing, too!

The king turned to the woodman. "You have succeeded where many have failed," he said. "You have only to name your reward."

The woodman shook his head. "I desire nothing, Your Majesty," he replied, "for I have all that a man can want—a home, a good wife, and three happy children. Our only aim is to make others happy too; and my children will gladly come to play with the princess."

From then onwards the sound of children's laughter echoed through the palace on many a day; and the little princess was never sad again.

Pantomime Pairs

Going to the pantomime is a very enjoyable Christmas treat and there are lots of pantomimes to go to see. Can you match up each person with an object associated with them in the pantomime?

LONDON

ANSWERS

ALADDIN AND HIS WONDERFUL LAMP, DICK WHITTINGTON AND HIS CAT, CINDERELLA AND HER GLASS SLIPPER, RED RIDING HOOD AND THE WOLF, SLEEPING BEAUTY AND HER SPINDLE, JACK AND THE BEANSTALK.

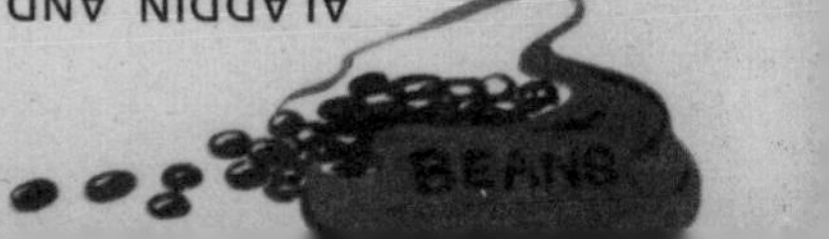

BEANS

Flower of the Night

A long, long time ago, on the rocky
slope of a hill in a far off country,
grew a little group of brightly coloured
flowers. They rustled and whispered
together as the breeze passed gently by.

The air echoed with their tinkling
laughter as they talked about the
day's happenings: about what they
had seen on the hillside and what
went on in the little village.down in
the valley.

The sun was beginning to set and
the air was becoming colder. The
children who had played on the hillside had gone home and the evening
was quiet and still. Even the flowers
closed up their petals for the night and
went to sleep. All, that is, except one,
whose petals began to *open* as the
evening wore on. She was a beautiful
blue flower, but she was most unhappy.

"Why am I so different from the rest?" she would ask herself. "When all the other flowers go to sleep I have to wake up. Then when they wake up I have to go to sleep."

A bird, on his way home to his nest and family, heard her.

"You are a little night flower," he told her. "You scent the air with your delicate perfume. Why, I always fly home this way in the evening. Your beautiful smell is my guide."

But the little blue flower was still sad.

"The children come up here to play," she said. "I never see them or hear their laughter. I don't ever see what goes on in the village, neither do I see the sheep which feed on the fresh green grass here."

"Well," said the bird, "God made you as you are and He must have had a reason. Don't be too sad, little flower. Goodnight." And off he flew to his wife and family.

"Perhaps if I try very hard I might be able to stay awake in the morning," said the blue flower to herself.

But try as she might she could *not* keep awake. As the sun rose so her petals closed and the next thing she knew was the chatter of her friends.

"The children have been here again," they told her, "and one little boy has been allowed to go with his father and the other shepherds up into the hills to stay with the sheep."

"Oh dear," sighed the little blue flower, "I miss everything that happens."

And as her little companions closed up their petals for the night she turned her face up to the sky which was now becoming quite dark. Her little friend the bird had already gone home and everywhere was quiet and peaceful.

As the stars began to appear she was puzzled at the appearance of one much larger and brighter than the rest. She thought she knew *all* the stars.

"What a beautiful bright star," she thought to herself.

In the distance she could hear a lamb bleating, then all was quiet again.

Then suddenly she was startled by what happened next. The sky was filled with a dazzling light and a very bright being appeared.

"Fear not," said a voice. Was the Voice speaking to her? There it was again. "For behold, I bring you good tidings of great joy, which shall be to you and to all people. For unto you is born this day in the city of David, a Saviour which is Christ the Lord, and this shall be a sign unto you. You shall find the Babe wrapped in swaddling clothes and lying in a manger."

And the air was filled with heavenly singing. The little flower had never known anything like it. Gradually, the light and the singing died away.

But what was that? She thought she heard voices again. Yes, footsteps too, coming nearer. It was the shepherds! They too had heard the strange new Voice, for she heard one shepherd say, "We can only take a little lamb, for it is all we have."

Then she saw them. They were coming along the track which led right past the little rocky mound on which she grew. And with them was the little boy who had been allowed to go up into the hills with them.

Oh, wouldn't she have something to tell her flower friends in the morning! What an exciting happening they had missed.

Now, as they approached the place where the flowers grew, the little boy stopped and looked at the blue flower.

"I will take this for the new baby," he said, and he very carefully picked her. He carried her gently in his hand, stumbling now and then on the stony pathway as he tried to keep up with the shepherds.

"Why, they are going to Bethlehem," thought the little blue flower. For was not that the City of David of which the Voice had spoken?

No longer was the little blue flower unhappy. She was bursting with pride. This must be a very special baby.

They soon came to Bethlehem and across the courtyard of an inn came a shaft of light from a nearby stable.

"That must be the place," said one shepherd.

"Aye, there's a manger right enough," said another.

And so it was that they came to where the baby lay, with Mary his mother, and Joseph, just as the Voice had told them.

The shepherds crept quietly into the stable and placed the little lamb at the foot of the manger. The little boy followed, clutching the beautiful blue flower. He held it out to the baby and Mary took it and smiled her thanks as she placed her hand on his head.

How happy the little blue flower felt.

"I said God must have had a reason," chirped a little voice which the flower knew.

And there was her friend the bird, perched on the stable door.

DEAR

Oh, listen, my dolly, and hear something new,
You're not to repeat it, 'tis only for you;
Naughty pussy has stolen grandfather's shoe,
And Topsy has painted my little dog blue!

Hush, baby, my dolly, I pray you don't cry,
And I'll give you some bread, and some milk by-and-by;
Or perhaps you'd like custard, or maybe a tart.
Then to either you are welcome, with all my heart.

DOLLY

Baby, my dolly, oh, she never cries!
Lie still, my darling, and close your little eyes!
Mummy must go, dear, and look for the others —
All the dear sisters, and all the dear brothers.

Little girl Polly
Said, "See my new dolly,
She has beautiful pop-open eyes;
But I can't make her speak,
Though I've tried for a week;
And whenever I hug her, she cries!"

The House in the SHOE

THE STORY OF THE NURSERY RHYME

"Come along, children, this is no time to lie sleeping in bed. We're moving into our new house today."

Mrs. Muffin bustled off to get the breakfast, and soon the children came rushing down the stairs and sat round the table to eat their porridge. There were so many children that they couldn't all sit down together, and some of them were feeling very hungry by the time it was their turn.

When they had all finished they ran upstairs and folded up their clothes and packed them into large linen bags: blue for the boys and pink for the girls. Of course, the youngest boy had lost his teddy bear, but at last it was found, in the airing cupboard, where he had put it to dry because it had fallen into the bath the previous night.

With their bags over their shoulders the children ran out of the door and into the lane, and Mrs. Muffin counted them as they went through the gate. They were so excited to see their new home that they nearly forgot the little black cat who, of course, didn't want to be left behind.

After locking the door Mrs. Muffin climbed into the donkey cart, which was laden with pots and pans and tables and chairs, and on top of it all was the kitchen stove. A last look round and off they set as the clock in the church tower struck ten.

The road wound through fields and woods, and the little donkey trotted happily along until they came to a stream which they had to cross. Then he just refused to move!

The children took off their socks and shoes and tried to pull him and push him.

Mrs. Muffin shook the reins and shouted, "Get along there."

But the donkey stayed just where he was.

Mrs. Muffin was wondering whether she could climb down from her high seat on top of all the furniture without falling into the stream, when the eldest boy, Thomas, had a bright idea.

He took a carrot out of the vegetable bag and held it in front of the donkey's nose. What a change! Thomas walked backwards, holding out the carrot, and the donkey splashed happily through the stream, pulling the cart behind him.

Around the next corner they went and there, in the middle of a large cabbage field, was their new home.

It wasn't a castle and it wasn't a house. It wasn't a cottage, either. It was a very, very large shoe!

Mrs. Muffin stopped the donkey cart and climbed down from her seat on top of the furniture. She put a ladder up against the toe of the shoe, while Thomas gave the little donkey the carrot and turned him loose in the field.

The boys carried up the furniture and pots and pans, and put the kitchen stove in the heel of the shoe, where the smoke could go out of the chimney. Then the girls followed with the bedding and the large pink and blue linen bags. Up the ladder they went, across the toe and up the laces and down into the shoe.

While they made up the beds they could smell the fine cabbage soup and freshly-baked bread that Mrs. Muffin was preparing for their supper.

What an excellent meal it was! And the shoe was so large that there was

plenty of room for them all to sit down together. After supper, Mrs. Muffin tucked them up in their beds and told them to go straight to sleep.

But the three youngest boys crept out through a hole in the side of the shoe and played hide-and-seek amongst the cabbages in the bright moonlight. They had such a fine game, and only just scrambled back into bed in time, before Mrs. Muffin went round with a candle to see that all was quiet before she went to bed.

Luckily she didn't notice that three little pairs of shoes were wet from the evening dew.

Soon all the children were fast asleep, dreaming of all the exciting things they would do the next day.

Mrs. Muffin blew out the candle, and the only light came from the moon as it filtered through the laces. But by the warm stove there were two little green stars, where the black cat sat, keeping watch in case any curious fieldmice should dare to invade his new home.

TINY TIM

IN the heart of Winberry Wood lived the Little People. Their king was a tiny manikin not two feet high, whose palace was built in the secret clearing hedged round with blackberry bushes.

It was a wonderful palace made of fallen pine cones, but very few of the Little People ever saw it for his Majesty's little sentries stood faithfully on guard at every bush.

But King Sylvanus was kind and loved his little subjects, and on sunny summer days he would order the silver chimes to be rung from the palace belfry. Then the Little People, in their rustic houses under the ferns, would drop their work and run out into the grassy paths to cheer at the top of their piping voices, crying: "The King has granted us a holiday. Hurrah, hurrah!"

At that the tiny cobblers, farmers, and blacksmiths would

tumble out of doors with their children and spend the day dancing and picnicking among the arum lilies and ragged robin.

It was on such a holiday one midsummer day that everyone was out of doors except Tiny Tim, the cobbler's youngest son. His father had ordered him to stay behind to cut out leather pieces for the workshop.

Poor Tim! Nobody loved him or seemed to care for him, for he was always getting his work in a muddle and everything he did seemed to turn out wrong. His four elder brothers, who were handsome and clever, teased him for his slownesses and called him Little Ugly One because his face was brown and wrinkled.

One day Tim decided to be useful in some way. He longed to hear his brothers say: " How clever you are, Tiny Tim!" And he thought if he tried hard enough he might succeed in pleasing them.

So he went outside and sat quietly beneath a frond of green bracken to think of a plan.

Then at length he remembered how his brothers had wished to have a young fir tree planted in their garden.

" I will plant one for them," thought Tim, as he jumped to his feet and ran to the shed for a spade. Before long he had dug up a tiny fir tree from the hill beyond the wood. Although it was so small, the sapling's roots had stretched deep into the ground and Tim tugged and pulled with all his might and main before he was able to get it out and carry it home.

When at last the tree was firmly planted in the garden Tim felt very hot and tired, but it cheered him to think how pleased his brothers would be when they saw it.

While he waited for them to come home Tim found a pot of paint lying in the garden shed. So he carefully painted the old shelf in the cobbler's shop.

" Father will be pleased," he thought, when his work was done.

Now it was time for the brothers to return, so Tim sat beside the front door and gazed at the pretty green needles of the little fir tree in the garden.

But, sad to say, when they saw the tree Tim's brothers were very angry.

"Just look at this!" cried Rollo, the eldest boy, " Little Ugly Face has uprooted our new seed bed and planted a stunted little tree. How dare he spoil the garden in this way."

Tim's father was angry too, when he saw the painted shelf. " I will not be able to use it for three days, and I will have to lay my pieces of leather on the floor till the paint dries."

How they grumbled at little Tim! At last he could bear it no longer and he crept sadly away to a distant grove of silver birch trees, where he sat on a large dock leaf and cried bitterly.

After a time the white moon sailed across the darkening sky and the woodland creatures cuddled down in their holes to rest; for now it was night. And little Tim crouched beneath the green bracken and cried himself to sleep.

Now it so happened that the grove was not far from the pine cone palace, though Tim was much too unhappy to remember that.

In the middle of the night King Sylvanus had a terrible dream. He dreamed that he was being chased by a horrible black giant who wanted to eat him for dinner. The King twitched and turned so much in his sleep that he fell out of bed and awoke with a dreadful start.

"Oh dear, oh dear, what a nightmare I have had," he gasped, still quaking with fright. And he was afraid to go to sleep again in case the dream should return.

So he put on his royal dressing gown and his purple slippers and crept quietly past the sleeping guards in the courtyard and entered the grove of birch trees to take a stroll in the moonlight.

Along came two little sentinels in coats of red, and cried: "Who goes there?"

But the King told them to return to their posts by the black-berry bushes as he wished to walk alone in the wood.

He walked to the end of the birch grove. The soft, cool night wind blew on his hot forehead and soon he had forgotten the dreadful nightmare. As he passed a clump of bracken the rustle of the King's footsteps woke Tiny Tim. He rubbed his sleepy eyes and peeped out from his hiding place.

"Surely this is the King himself," gasped the little fellow.

Then, suddenly, there was a noise like thunder, as through the wood stamped the black giant who had lain asleep under the dark mountain for a hundred years and had now come down to the wood to find something to eat. The first person the hungry giant saw was the King of the Little People.

Just as the giant bounded forward to seize the King, Tiny Tim threw himself at the monster's huge feet. Down the giant fell with a tremendous crash, his head landing in a bog. There he lay on the grass, bellowing with surprise and rage, while the guards from the blackberry hedge rushed out and bound him fast from top to toe.

"Well done, my little fellow!" cried King Sylvanus. And the guards carried Tim shoulder high to the palace, where the King brought out his tiny golden sword. Bidding Tim kneel before him, Sylvanus tapped him lightly on each shoulder, saying: "Arise Sir Tim, Knight of Sylvanus, King of the Little People!"

Tiny Tim's heart glowed with love for the King. Here, at last, was someone who cared for him. His tiny brown face was wrinkled in one large smile of happiness.

As the sun rose over the wood the silver chimes rang out from the belfry. The Little People scrambled excitedly into their clothes and hastened out of doors as a gay procession wound through the trees.

"The King! The King!" cried the cobbler and his four sons. Then they almost fainted with astonishment as they caught sight of Sir Tim. He was seated on a prancing white pony, his clothes were of rich velvet, and he bore on his sleeve the golden badge of Knighthood.

From that day onwards faithful Sir Tim lived at the palace as the bodyguard of the King.

Fairy Hats

Did you know that all the fairyfolk have their own special kinds of hats?

Elves wear little caps of elfin green, and some elves have a jaunty, red feather of their cap. This is a wishing feather and enables the elf to make one wish a day which will come true. The wishing feather is given by the Fairy Queen herself as a reward to the elf for some kind deed. The wish can only be used to bring happiness to some other person, and should some naughty elf use it badly the feather will lose all its magic power and turn an ugly shade of purple.

Leprechauns, too, wear bright green hats, but these have a large golden circle at the front, representing the crock of gold which a leprechaun guards at the end of the rainbow.

Pixies, who are often named after flowers and trees, usually wear caps and hats made from the petals and leaves of their namesake. Pixie Holly has a glistening red cap of bright holly berries, Pixie Bluebell has a smart blue helmet, very similar to the one worn by Pixie Foxglove, while little Pixie Primrose has a dainty yellow bonnet.

As you might imagine, the nixies, the fairy folk who live in, or near water. choose water colours for their hats. They wear little caps of gleaming blues, greens and greys, shot with silver . . . and the nixies can go swimming in their caps and never get them wet.

Many of the goblins are old and wise, and wear dignified hats, in sombre colours, as tall as a church steeple. All, that is, except Goblin Greensleeves who wears a patchwork hat in every shade of green to match the jacket which gives him his name.

Fairies wear many different kinds of hats, made from such delicate materials as thistledown, moonshine and flower petals. All the hats are made by the fairy milliner, Fairy Stitchwort, who lives in Pincushion Park, and every hat is different, so that every fairy has a hat which is specially her own, which pleases all the fairies very much.

A HAT FOR ALL SEASONS

The gnomes like to wear a different hat for each season of the year. They wear green in spring, yellow in summer, brown and red in autumn, and snow-white caps in winter.

You may perhaps have seen the hats the gnomes wear without recognising them. Their spring hats become acorn cups, the fields are strewn with the yellow cups which were once the gnomes' summer hats—some fairies used these to hold butter—and the wind tossed their autumn hats about until they became russet leaves. But the pretty snow caps of the gnomes were carefully tended by Dame Nature herself, and became the first snowdrops of the year.

Imps are rather naughty little fairies, up to all kinds of tricks, but they are very willing helpers for the Man in the Moon. They are dressed from top to toe in the shining black of the night sky, with little round black caps to match. Because of this they can fly around the sky carrying messages from the Man in the Moon to the stars, and helping to keep all the stars brightly polished.

A SHOOTING STAR

When he is particularly pleased with an imp, the Man in the Moon gives him a silver star to pin on his cap. This means, of course, that from time to time new stars appear in the sky, and sometimes the imps use these stars for returning to fairyland when they have worked very hard. You might even see them, but because of their black clothes all you see is the star shooting down from the heavens . . . we call it a shooting star.

Brownies, as their name suggests, are usually dressed in brown, with gay little hats of yellow and red, trimmed with beech leaves. Although most brownies are busy helping the farmers to make butter and cheese in the dairy, some brownies are also given a special job by Dame Nature. She asks them to look after all the woodland animals, especially those that go to sleep in the winter. These brownies, instead of wearing coloured caps, wear brown caps

made from nutshells which are decorated with dried poppy seeds painted in different colours.

Finally, there are the trolls who live beneath the ground searching for precious jewels. These ugly little men are always afraid that someone will steal their treasure, so they make lots of different hats all covered in bright jewels which they wear all the time. When they are not wearing one of their hats they keep them in a strongly-locked box, and always have the key to this box on a golden chain around their necks.

HEARTS

When baby Jesus was born in the stable in Bethlehem His mother, Mary, laid Him gently in a manger full of hay because she had no cradle to put Him in.

But the hay felt rough to Jesus and He whimpered as He slept. So Mary looked around the stable for something soft to make a pillow and coverlet for her baby.

Growing just outside the stable door was a cluster of tiny white daisies, and as Mary reached the doorway they called out shyly to her. "Dear lady, please pick us and use us to make a pillow and soft cover for your dear babe," they begged. "Our petals are soft and we will not hurt Him."

So Mary picked enough of the dainty white flowers to cover the rough hay and to make a soft pillow for Jesus, and from that moment He slept sweetly.

# of GOLD

When the time came for the Holy Family to leave the stable, Mary bent down and showed her little Son the cluster of flowers by the door. "Here are the kind flowers that made you comfortable, my Son," she said gently. "Truly they have hearts of gold."

The daisies blushed to hear themselves praised, and the tips of their petals were stained pink. Then, as Jesus touched them gently with His tiny fingers, there appeared in the centre of each white daisy a shining golden heart.

So next time you see a daisy growing in a field or on a lawn, look at it closely. You will see that it still has its golden heart and its pink-tipped petals to remind everyone of the kind deed it performed so many years ago on the very first Christmas of all.

One Summer's Day

Quite by chance, one summer's day,
I spied beneath some tall trees
A small walnut-shell cradle
Swaying gently in the breeze.

There was no one else in sight,
So I quickly had a peep,
And saw a baby fairy
Lying there, fast asleep.

A skylark far above her head
Sang her a lullaby,
And as she dreamed so sweetly,
She gave a happy little sigh.

Then, suddenly, she awakened,
And a lovely smile gave me,
But, alas, I could not linger—
Mummy called me home to tea.

Jeremy visits the Sultan

Jeremy awoke suddenly and listened. Then he ran to the window. Out of the mist above the tree tops there appeared a little old man on a shaggy pony galloping towards him. It was the little old man who had given him a twisty-coloured stick of chalk. It was red and blue, and green and yellow, and when Jeremy rolled it backwards and forwards between his fingers and thumb the colours seemed to flow first one way and then another. It was magic chalk, because if you drew an ancient building on the garden wall with ordinary white chalk and the door last of all with the twisty-coloured chalk, you could open the door and go through it into some wonderful adventure.

But Jeremy had lost the twisty-coloured chalk. He couldn't find it anywhere.

"It's time to draw another door ... another door," the little old man cried as he drew nearer to the window and the shaggy little pony spun round to gallop off.

"I've lost the chalk!" Jeremy shouted, for the pony was already pawing the ground.

"Look on the ledge under the sundial," the little old man cried, and was gone so quickly that he was out of sight in a flash.

Jeremy was so excited that he could

hardly wait to finish his breakfast before hurrying into the garden.

The magic chalk *was* under the sun-dial!

"I'll draw an Eastern palace like the one in the picture at Granny's," he thought. "I've always wanted to know what it's like inside, and I'll use my ordinary chalks for everything except the door; I mustn't forget that."

The smooth, flat surface of the garden wall was a fine place to draw on, and in about half an hour Jeremy had drawn a large and splendid Eastern palace with a tower so tall that he had to stand on his tiptoes to finish it. There were some palm trees on one side and a river flowed close by. All was finished except for the door.

"Now," he decided as he took the twisty-coloured chalk out of his top pocket, "I'll draw the door."

But, just in time, he remembered that it is so hot in the Eastern countries that the great palace doors would be open in the daytime and there would be lots and lots of guards to stop any-one just walking in.

It almost looked as if he had made a mistake and should have drawn some-thing else.

Then he remembered that in Granny's picture there was a little door in the palace wall close to the foot of the tall tower.

"That's it!" he thought, and quickly he drew the large doors with his ordinary chalks and then the small door – which had a pointed top – with the very special chalk.

"There won't be any guards here to stop me; I'll just push it open and walk in."

At first he gave a gentle push because it was such a little door. But it wouldn't open. Then he pushed harder and harder, and at last he put his shoulder against it and pushed with all his might. It was no use, the door was as tightly shut as ever and he was still outside the palace.

He wondered what could have gone wrong, because he had drawn the door very carefully. Then all at once he saw that he'd forgotten something. Doors in Eastern palaces always had large fancy hinges with scrolls and curves, and they were fastened on with big, square-headed nails.

Of course, that was the reason. You couldn't expect a door, even one drawn with the twisty-coloured chalk, to open if it hadn't any hinges.

It didn't take long to put things right and when he had drawn the hinges he pushed again, and this time the door opened a little way. Another hard push and he was inside the palace at last. But instead of the blaze of splendour he had expected, he found himself in a rather dark, narrow passage.

"Oh dear," he thought, feeling just a tiny bit frightened, "I don't like this passage. I wonder if it leads to the Wizard's den. There is sure to be a Wizard here; Eastern palaces all have them, especially old ones like this. Perhaps he lives in the tall, square tower. I'm going on anyway, and if I do meet the Wizard I'll pretend I'm in an awful hurry!"

But the passage didn't lead to the Wizard's den. He had not gone far when he came to a room where six or seven dark men, whom he took to be palace servants, were piling some of the most luscious fruit he had ever seen on to silver trays. He soon saw, however, that they were not servants, for they wore large, heavy ear-rings of gold, and were dressed in brightly-coloured silk trousers gathered tight round the ankles, and funny little short coats trimmed with gold lace. Round their heads they wore white turbans. Their shoes weren't really shoes at all; they were like slippers with sharp toes which pointed straight up in the air.

Jeremy wondered if they came on camels and brought the fruit as a present for the Sultan. Perhaps they were going to take it to him now. He wished they would let him help them, then *he* could go to see the Sultan too.

In a minute or two a trumpet sounded from somewhere and the men quickly lifted the silver trays and, forming a procession, went towards a door at the other end of the room. Three boys about Jeremy's age, whom he had not noticed before, joined in at the end of the procession, and as they all moved slowly off, the last boy saw Jeremy and beckoned to him to come with them.

"They must be going to the Sultan," Jeremy thought joyfully, and as he took his place at the end of the procession he saw that the boys were also carrying presents – the first a golden goblet, the second a silver chain, and the third a jewelled ring.

"Oh dear," Jeremy said to himself,

"I ought to be taking a present too."

He looked around for something to take, but there was no time to lose and he couldn't see anything suitable. He searched his pockets hurriedly. It would be dreadful to appear before the Sultan empty-handed. Ah! here was something which might do. It was only a bent-wire puzzle which, if you knew how, you could take apart, but it was a jolly good one and not many grown-ups could do it until you showed them, and then they couldn't always do it again.

The door through which the procession passed led into the biggest room

Jeremy had ever seen, and in the middle was an enormous table with piles and piles of food and curiously-shaped jars of wine on it.

A great feast was going on, and around the table sat many dark-skinned men and ladies of high rank, dressed in rich silks. They were laughing and talking as they feasted. At the head of the table, seated cross-legged on a kind of low couch with a brightly-coloured canopy over the top, was a man whose dress was far more splendid than any other, and when he spoke everyone listened respectfully.

"That must be the Sultan," Jeremy thought. "I'd like to get near enough to see what he's really like. I've never seen a Sultan . . . at least only in a book." And then he saw that the procession he was in was going right to the head of the table.

Each of the men paused a moment before the Sultan, who touched his gift to show that he was pleased to accept it, and then passed on. But when the boys held up their gifts, the Sultan took them one by one in his hands and looked carefully at them . . . first the golden goblet, next the silver chain, and then the jewelled ring. All of these seemed to please him.

Then came Jeremy's turn. Feeling rather excited he offered his bent-wire puzzle. The Sultan frowned.

"Oh dear, he doesn't like it," Jeremy thought, all his excitement going in a flash. "He thinks I'm giving him a bit of iron instead of gold or precious stones. I'd better show him how it works, he won't have seen one like this before. I do hope it pleases him or he may have me cast into the dungeons."

Holding the wire puzzle up so that the Sultan could see it clearly, Jeremy twisted the two halves in just exactly the right way and they slid apart easily. Then he put them together again and handed the puzzle to the Sultan, as if to say, "Here, you try!" But he didn't say it, of course. You don't *say* things like that to Sultans, ever.

As he watched, the frown cleared from the Sultan's face and he took the puzzle from Jeremy, but instead of trying to do it himself he gave it to the man seated next to him, who took it with a smile and a bow as if to say, "Just watch me, I can do this easily." His smile soon faded, however, as he twisted and turned the puzzle first this way and then that, for however hard he tried he couldn't slide the two halves apart as Jeremy had done.

By now everyone was watching with great interest and other hands were stretched out for the puzzle. But though lots of people tried, none of them could do it. When at last it was handed back to Jeremy and he took it apart as easily as before there were excited murmurs of applause.

While all this was going on, the Sultan had sent a messenger out of the room, and now he returned with the very man Jeremy had wondered about when he first entered the palace . . . the Wizard!

He was a tall man, with piercing black eyes and a long beard, and he was dressed in a black cloak which reached to his feet. On his head he wore a tall, pointed black hat with magical signs painted on it, and a big golden star right on the very top. In his hand he carried a long staff, on which three serpents were painted, their tails nearly on the ground and their bodies twined round and round as if they were climbing up it, and the knob at the top was carved into the shape of an eye and set with small brilliant stones which twinkled in the sunlight.

"He looks a very powerful kind of Wizard," Jeremy thought. "I hope he's not unfriendly."

Then, to his dismay, he saw that the Wizard looked *most* unfriendly, for the Sultan had handed the wire puzzle to him and he didn't look at all sure that he could do it. The Sultan told him that if he couldn't separate the two parts as Jeremy had done, then, according to Eastern custom, Jeremy would be proclaimed the greater Wizard.

Now to be Chief Wizard at a Sultan's palace would seem to be a wonderful thing, but Jeremy didn't even know any conjuring tricks, let alone magic such as Wizards used. It would be better to show them how the puzzle worked and tell them that he wasn't any sort of Wizard at all.

He was just about to do this when a slave rushed in and fell at the Sultan's feet, crying that the Queen's favourite dog was lost. This caused great excitement and everybody began talking at once. But the Sultan called for silence and then commanded the Wizard to tell them where the dog was.

This suited the Wizard very well indeed, for now he need not attempt to do the puzzle. He hurriedly pushed it into an inner pocket in his cloak.

"I say, that's mine, you know," Jeremy protested. "And besides, you'll never be able to do it by yourself. I don't believe you're a bit clever!"

No one, however, paid any attention to what he said. A servant had brought a small lamp, and the Wizard was casting into the flame some powder, which flared up with a blue flash like a firework. He began to wave his hands about and chant some queer-sounding words in a high, thin voice. Everyone seemed to think this was very wonderful. But Jeremy thought it was silly to try to find a lost dog by singing a song; he nearly laughed aloud.

The Wizard's chant ended suddenly and he led the way up some steps on to the flat roof of the palace. The Sultan and all the people followed him, and Jeremy went too because he wanted to see what would happen.

As soon as they were on the roof the people formed a ring round the Wizard, who began to sniff the air in all directions, turning round and round as he did so. Then he held out his long staff with the three serpents painted on it, so that the knob which was carved into an eye pointed first to the north and then to the south. He muttered and shook his head.

Then he pointed the staff to the east, and immediately it shook violently in his hand and the people cheered. He told them that the eye had seen the lost dog and it would be found in that direction within a thousand spear-lengths.

So swift runners were sent to the east. But while everyone was watching their progress with great interest, Jeremy managed to edge his way un-noticed out of the ring of people, towards the low wall which ran round the edge of the roof.

"Now," he said to himself as he climbed on to the wall, "I'll look with my real eyes, not with a wooden one on the end of a stick like that silly old Wizard! Wouldn't he be surprised if I found the Queen's little dog all by myself? I'll look really hard while they all have their backs to me."

He shaded his eyes with his hand and looked at the miles and miles of gardens which stretched all round the palace. He couldn't see any sign of the little dog, but there was *something* a long, long way off, something moving rapidly towards the palace.

Jeremy looked very hard, very hard indeed. He almost knew what to expect, for he had a strange, all-alive feeling inside, a feeling that came just before the sound of galloping hoofs reached his ears. Yes, there he was, far away in the distance . . . the little old man on his shaggy pony, tearing towards the palace like a whirlwind.

"I wonder what he's coming to tell me?" Jeremy thought, feeling in the top pocket of his blazer to make sure that the twisty-coloured stick of chalk was still safely tucked there.

Nearer and nearer the little old man galloped, and when he was still quite a long way off he stopped and raised his arm.

Jeremy held his breath and listened. At first he couldn't hear anything; then the little old man's voice came faintly over the distance.

"Look under the cedar tree . . . Beware of the Wizard!"

The next moment the shaggy little pony turned and galloped away so furiously that it was gone in a flash.

Jeremy got down quietly from the low wall on to the roof. There was no need to be extra-specially careful,

because everyone was still looking the other way watching the progress of the swift runners.

"No one has seen or heard anything," he thought, as he crept down the steps and out into the palace gardens. "I'll go and look under the cedar tree where the little old man said. But I *must* remember to beware of the Wizard. That's awfully important or he wouldn't have said so."

It took Jeremy quite five minutes to reach the cedar tree, but there, curled up against the trunk and very fast asleep, was a little brown dog. He took it up in his arms and hurried back to the palace. As he climbed the steps on to the flat roof he was just in time to hear the Sultan order the swift runners to be cast into the dungeons because they had failed to find the Queen's dog.

"Oh, please don't do that, Sir Sultan," Jeremy cried. "I've got the dog here. I found it. It wasn't where the Wizard said at all; it was under the cedar tree."

Everyone stared in amazement as the little dog leapt from Jeremy's arms and, with a joyful bark, ran straight to the Queen.

The Wizard looked so unfriendly that Jeremy almost expected him to burst, and he wished he'd remembered the little old man's warning. But he had been in such a hurry to save the swift runners from being cast into the dungeons that he'd quite forgotten to be careful.

"Reward him greatly," the Queen said, as she fondled the little dog. "Make him the Chief Wizard and let the old Wizard be flung headlong from the tall tower!"

"Oh dear, this is terrible," Jeremy thought, as two slaves ran forward and seized the Wizard. "I can't let them do that even if he is unfriendly; and besides, they might fling *me* headlong from the tall tower when they find I can't do everything. And I can't— there's lots I don't know. Whatever can I do to save him?"

He tried to think of something very quickly. Then, all at once he had an idea.

"Stop!" he called in a loud voice, so loud that the Sultan frowned, for no one *ever* spoke like that in his presence. But Jeremy pretended not to notice and went on, "Before you take the Wizard away I have a surprise for you."

All the people now watched Jeremy as he took the twisty-coloured chalk from his pocket and went towards the highest part of the wall which ran round the palace roof. Quickly he drew a narrow door like the one in his own garden wall. Then he turned round and said to the Sultan, but in a voice loud enough for everyone to hear, "First, promise not to throw the Wizard from the tall tower until you see me again."

When the Sultan had promised – for he thought Jeremy wanted to show the Wizard how clever he was – Jeremy pushed at the little magic door. The next second he was back in his own garden. But he heard a tiny bark of farewell from the little dog who, although he could not talk, was really wiser than the Sultan or the Queen or the Wizard.

Fairy Flowers

A fairy dandelion clock
Never loudly says *Tick-tock!*
Fairies have to puff away
To find out the time of day.

The pretty scarlet pimpernel
Forecasts the weather very well.
If open wide . . . sunny and fine,
Tight petals . . . a wet weather sign!

And the cornfield poppies keep
The soot left by the fairy sweep;
While the daisies have hearts of gold
For their kind deeds in days of old.

Roses are Queen Mab's own flowers,
Their petals bedeck her fairy bowers,
Soft as silk, of every hue,
Arrayed with jewels of glistening dew.

The CROSS PRINCESSES

THERE was once an old king who had three pretty daughters. He was very fond of them. But the three were always quarrelling, so everyone in the land called them the Cross Princesses.

There was nothing in the world that the old king did not wish to give them. He even went to the fairy queen to beg for them a favour each.

" What are these three princesses like?" asked the fairy queen. " If I know something about each girl I shall know better what to give them."

" Amy, the youngest, wears white shoes," said the king. " She is very fond of pretty clothes, and would like nothing better than a nice dress. Ella wears blue shoes. She is very fond of flowers, and she would like a fairy rose bush for her garden. And Una, the eldest, loves animals. But I leave you to guess what sort of animal would best suit a royal palace."

The king said nothing about their haughty tempers. He was afraid if he did so the fairy queen might do nothing for them.

"Very well," said the fairy queen, "I will do what I can to make each girl happy. Let each one go alone to the wood, first wade in the wishing pond, then go to the old witch to receive a fairy gift. The witch will know what to give each without asking."

Now a playful little elf named Puck was playing in the fairy wood while the king was talking to the fairy queen and he heard every word.

"It would be much better if the king had asked the fairy queen to make them better friends," Puck told his little elf friends. "She little knows they are called the Cross Princesses."

Meanwhile the fairy queen arranged to keep her promise.

She went to the witch in the wood and said to her, "When a pretty girl comes to you wearing white shoes, give her this fairy dress of white satin." And she handed the witch a dress which shone like the stars.

"When a pretty girl comes to you wearing blue shoes, give her this fairy rose bush." And she handed the witch a little bush

which would bloom all the year round with roses of every colour.

"When a pretty girl comes to you wearing red shoes, give her this white kitten." And she handed the witch a blue-eyed kitten with long white hair softer than silk.

"It shall be done, Your Majesty," said the witch, with a curtsy.

None of them knew that the playful Puck had made up his mind to change things.

The three princesses kissed the old king when he told them they would each receive a fairy gift. They were really only cross to one another.

Amy went first to the fairy wood. She took off her white shoes so that they would not get wet, before stepping into the wishing pond. When she had waded in it a few minutes she came out to put on her shoes.

She could not find them. Puck had hidden them away. She had to give up the search.

"Ah well, never mind," thought the princess. "I will go to the witch and receive my fairy gift as my father was promised. Perhaps I shall find my shoes when I come back."

Away went Princess Amy and knocked at the witch's door.

"Come in," cried the old witch, who was expecting her.

The witch looked down to see what colour shoes she wore, and saw that her feet were bare.

" Get out," cried the old witch. " I have nothing to give you." With that the witch pushed Princess Amy out of the door and banged it.

The poor little princess was ashamed to go home without her fairy gift. She did not know why it was refused her. So she hid in a hollow tree, not very far away, from which she could peep out and see what would happen to her sisters.

Ella went next to the fairy wood. She took off her blue shoes and stepped into the wishing pond. After wading in the pond a few minutes she stepped out to put on her shoes.

She could not find her own blue shoes. She found Amy's white ones instead, for Puck had put the white ones near the pond and hidden her own blue ones away.

" Ah, well, thought Princess Ella, " I thought I had on my own shoes, but Amy must be wearing them. We must have changed shoes this morning. We will change back again tomorrow."

With that, she put on the white shoes, and away she went to the witch's door. She knocked, and the old witch opened it.

Seeing the girl's white shoes, the old witch said, " Welcome, my dear, I have a lovely gift for you, one you are sure to like."

The witch brought out the white satin dress, which shone like the stars, and gave it to Princess Ella.

The princess thanked her kindly, and went away. But she was disappointed, for she would have dearly loved some fairy flowers for the garden under her window at the palace.

But little Princess Amy, hiding in the hollow tree, sighed as she saw the white satin dress Ella carried away, for it was the very thing she had wished for herself.

Then Una went to the fairy wood. She took off her red shoes and laid them down beside the wishing pond before she stepped in it. When she had waded a few minutes she came out to put on her shoes again.

Puck had been busy and had made another exchange. All Una could find was Ella's blue shoes. So Una thought she and Ella had put on each other's shoes that morning. She did not even look for her own. She put on the blue ones and went gaily along to the witch's door.

When the witch saw her wearing blue shoes, she said, " Welcome, my dear, and receive the fairy rosebush which blooms all the year round, and the scent of which will rise up and fill your room."

The girl took it and thanked her. But she was puzzled to know

what the witch meant for, unlike her sister Ella, Princess Una had no flower garden under her window. She was disappointed too, for roses, magic or otherwise, did not interest her at all.

After that, the old witch waited and waited, expecting a third princess to call wearing red shoes. But none came.

It was near nightfall and still poor little Amy hid in the hollow tree, ashamed to go back to her palace home with nothing, for she had seen both her sisters take away beautiful presents.

She became so sad that she sat down in the hollow tree and wept.

"What have I done that I deserve nothing?" she thought.

While Princess Amy wept in the hollow tree, the white kitten cried in the witch's hut. Having had nothing all day, it was very hungry and wanted a saucer of milk. But the greedy old witch had only enough for herself, and she would not give any to the poor little white kitten.

The noise of the kitten made her angry, and rather than give it her own milk she opened the door and drove it out into the wood.

When the witch had closed her door again for the night, little Amy crept from the hollow tree to comfort the kitten. She picked it up in her arms.

"You dear little thing," said Amy. "I will go home to the palace now for your sake to give you some milk."

She began to run home with the kitten as fast as she could, for she wanted to reach the palace before dark. As she passed beside the wishing pond she saw Princess Una's red shoes lying there, for Puck had put them out so that they might be found.

"Well, well," said Amy. "We have all picked up the wrong shoes today. I may as well wear these as carry them home."

When she arrived at the palace wearing the red shoes and carrying the pretty little white kitten in her arms, she heard her two sisters talking crossly. Ella wanted the rosebush which Una had. But Una did not want the satin dress in exchange.

"I do not like either of these presents much," cried Una. "I would not give a thank you for the satin dress or this rosebush. What I long for is a dear little animal to pet."

"If you do not like the rosebush give it to me," cried Ella.

"Why should you have what you like when I have not?" cried Una.

Just then, Amy walked in with the little kitten.

"Here is a little kitten for you, Una," she said. "It is hungry and needs feeding now. I will give you this, if you will give Ella the rosebush so that she will give me that lovely dress."

So the three princesses changed with each other, and each had the thing she wanted most. Having made each other happy once they were good friends for ever after, and were never again called the Cross Princesses.

1. Unscramble these names of fairy-type people. MENOG, IPIEX, LOBGIN, FEL, MIP and NOW-BRIE.

2. Which two faces are exactly the same?

3. Which is the odd one out?

4. What well-known proverb is illustrated here?

ANSWERS

1. Gnome, pixie, goblin, elf, imp and brownie. 2. Faces C and F are exactly the same. 3. The odd one out is the deer, all the other animals can be found on a farm. 4. Too many cooks spoil the broth.

ALADDIN and his Wonderful Lamp

Long ago, in China, there lived a poor widow woman who had a handsome son named Aladdin. One day Aladdin was walking through the marketplace when a richly dressed stranger came up and spoke to him.

"Are you Aladdin, son of Mustafa, the tailor?" asked the stranger, who was really a magician in disguise.

"Yes, but my father is dead," replied Aladdin.

"That is sad news, for I am his brother," replied the magician. "But take me to your mother, for I wish to talk to her."

Aladdin had never heard of an uncle, but his mother welcomed the stranger warmly and thanked him for the food and gifts he brought. She was overjoyed when the magician offered to adopt Aladdin as his son and teach him to become a merchant.

Next morning Aladdin set off with his uncle to his new home, each riding a fine horse. They travelled many miles until it grew dark. "We must stop and eat and rest a while," said Aladdin's uncle.

Aladdin lit a fire and then, to his amazement, the magician threw some strange powder on to the fire. He spoke some magic words and the fire vanished, and in its place was a large, flat stone with a ring in the middle. Aladdin was very frightened, but the magician told him to lift the stone and go down into the cavern beneath it and bring him up an old lamp which he would find there. "All the treasure you find shall be yours," added his uncle. "But before you go, put this ring on your finger."

Aladdin found the cave filled with gold and jewels and he quickly filled his pockets with these as he searched for the lamp. "Hurry up, boy," called his false uncle, impatiently. "Give me the lamp."

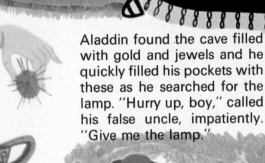

But Aladdin was a clever youth and he called back: "Not until I am safely out of this cave!" This so angered the magician that he closed the door of the cave and Aladdin was left inside.

Left alone, Aladdin wrung his hands in dismay. "What will become of me now?" he cried. But, suddenly, he touched the ring on his finger and a beautiful genie appeared before him. "I am the slave of the ring," she said. "What is your wish, O Master?"

"Take me and everything the cave contains back to my home," ordered Aladdin. In a trice Aladdin was back with his mother, who listened in wonder to his tale.

"With this money we shall be able to have a fine house, rich clothes and wonderful food!" she cried.

"Yes, I shall be so rich that I shall be able to ask for the hand of the Sultan's daughter," replied Aladdin. "For I have long loved her from afar."

The slave of the ring told Aladdin that if he rubbed the old lamp he had found in the cave, a really powerful genie would appear.

Aladdin rubbed the lamp and told the genie to bring gold and jewels for his mother to take to the palace as gifts for the princess.

The Sultan was so pleased with all these rich gifts that he willingly agreed that the princess should marry Aladdin. The wedding was celebrated in great splendour and Aladdin and his princess went to live in a magnificent palace, which was provided by the genie of the lamp.

Aladdin and his princess lived together happily for many months . . . but he never told her about his magic ring or the powers of the old lamp. One day he went off on a hunting trip, leaving the princess behind in the palace.

As the princess was resting on her balcony she heard someone calling in the street below:
"New lamps for old!
New lamps for old!"

She peered over the balcony and saw that it was an old lamp seller . . . but actually it was the wicked magician searching for the magic lamp.
"Take this old lamp belonging to my husband," she told a servant. "Ask that old man for a new one. It will be a lovely surprise for Aladdin when he comes home."

110

But the moment the magician got hold of the lamp he rubbed it and the genie appeared. "Take Aladdin's palace and the princess and myself to a faraway place where none can find us!" he ordered the genie, and in a trice his wish was granted.

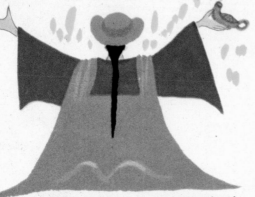

When Aladdin arrived home he was heart-broken at the disappearance of his palace and his bride, and the Sultan was very angry and ordered Aladdin to find her at once . . . or he would lose his head!

Aladdin rubbed his magic ring and sought the help of his pretty genie when she appeared. "Alas, O Master, my magic is not as powerful as that of the genie of the lamp!" she cried. "Yet although I cannot return your princess, I can take you to where she is. Also I can give you a magic potion which will make the magician sleep for ever."

"Oh, genie, please take me to my princess at once," cried Aladdin eagerly.

Suddenly Aladdin found himself in his palace gardens. Near a lily pond he saw his princess, weeping bitterly. "Do not cry, dear love," he said softly. "Drop the contents of this phial into the magician's wine and all will be well."

That night the princess dropped the sleeping draught into a goblet of wine and offered it to the magician. He drank it all, and a moment later fell into a deep sleep.

The princess quickly took the lamp from the folds of his cloak and gave it back to Aladdin, who immediately summoned the genie.

In a moment they were back home again. The Sultan was delighted to see his daughter again, and he made Aladdin his Grand Vizier. From then onwards Aladdin always made sure that his wonderful lamp was closely guarded and it was never stolen again. It brought Aladdin many riches and he and his princess lived happily together for the rest of their lives.

A FAIRY TREE

How would you like to grow a tree, the same size as the tiny trees in fairyland? Well, it's quite easy. All you need is a plant pot or a small glass jar. The bottom of the pot or jar should be covered with very small pebbles, then filled up with ordinary soil from the garden.

Now you have to decide what kind of tree you would like to grow. Orange, lemon or grapefruit; these are the easiest ones to start with. Suppose you choose to grow a tiny orange tree. First of all you save up the pips from your orange, and plant two or three in each pot. Put them very near to the top of the pot, just about a quarter-of-an-inch beneath the surface of the soil. Water them very carefully, until the soil is just moist, but not wet; perhaps mummy or daddy will help you with this.

Your pots should then be put in a warm, dark place, where the little pips should begin to sprout. Leave them there until the small shoots appear. When they can be seen, it is time to move your growing trees to a sunny windowsill, where the sunshine will help them to grow. Remember to water them well and don't allow them to go dry.

Your tiny tree will not have fruit on it, as do the trees in fairyland, but they will be very pretty, and sometimes it is possible to smell oranges or lemons from their leaves.

113

Season time

Spring is such a lovely time,
Gold primroses fill meadows green,
Birds are busy building nests,
And fleecy, new-born lambs are seen.

Summertime is full of fun,
On golden sands, near sea so blue,
I build a turreted castle grand,
And fish for shrimps in pools, do you?

Autumn is a mellow time,
When leaves turn yellow, russet, red;
And squirrels search for winter stores
Before going sleepily to bed.

Winter brings us Christmas time,
With lots of parties, presents too;
Toasted crumpets by the fire,
And skating on ponds of icy-blue.

THE LITTLE BELL

The two big bells in the church tower were very proud of themselves. They hung at the very top of the tower, and rang to tell the people in the little town of every service in the church. They rang every day before the morning service, and twice on Sundays, when there was an evening service as well. Sometimes, on very special occasions, they rang at other times—when people were married in the church, and when there were fairs and festivals in the town.

Now, in the church tower, just beneath the two big bells, there hung a little bell. He could not ring nearly so loud as the other two; and indeed it was so long since he had chimed at all that a great many people in the town did not even know that he was there. Every day he listened to the two big bells ringing out, and every day he wished that his own chance would come.

One Sunday afternoon, while the two big bells were snoozing, a flock

115

of birds flew over the church tower. They saw the two bells quietly hanging and decided to rest there. They flew down and fluttered over the bells, finding places to perch.

"What a stroke of luck!" twittered one of the birds. "We have been flying for nearly a week, looking for a new home where we can build our nests. This tower will suit us perfectly, and these two bells will make a perfect shelter."

So, while the bells slept through the afternoon, the birds flew busily about, collecting twigs and building their nests. When they awoke, the two big bells were amazed to see what had happened.

"This is terrible," they said to the birds. "There is a church service very soon and we must ring out to tell the people about it. We cannot ring at all if you keep your nests here."

Then the little bell had an idea.

"Listen," he shouted up to the two other bells, "*I* can ring to the people today! I am sure they will hear me if I try hard."

And straight away he began to swing up and down. It was such a long time since he had rung that he had to work terribly hard at first; but after a bit he was really enjoying himself, and ringing as loud as he could.

The people in the town stopped and listened.

"What a beautiful sound," they said to each other. "We have never heard a bell ring like that before. We must go and look in the church tower."

So they ran up to the church and crowded into the tower to see what was ringing. And what a surprise! There were the two big bells hanging very still, and covered with fluttering birds hopping in and out of their nests. And underneath was the little bell that everyone had forgotten, ringing as hard as he could.

The people stared and stared. And then they said to each other:

"How nice to have birds living in our tower! They must stay until they have laid their eggs and hatched them. While the birds are here, the big bells must keep very still and the little bell can ring for us. What a nice sound it makes."

"Thank you!" twittered the birds, as they flew about their new home.

"Thank you!" whispered the two big bells as they settled down to a nice long rest.

"Oh, thank you very much, everyone!" rang the little bell, happier than he had ever been before.

The REAL NURSERY RHYME PEOPLE

Did you know that many of the familiar nursery rhymes were written about real people?

A FINE QUEEN

The fine lady that a lot of people rode to Banbury to see was the first Queen Elizabeth, who was well-known for her lovely clothes made from satins and velvets, and who had many beautiful jewelled rings. It was the fashion in those days to have bells on the long, pointed toes of the shoes worn by court ladies, and although this may have made walking difficult, they certainly had music wherever they went, just as the rhyme said.

CONTRARY MARY

Because she was very gay and wore colourful clothes — one of her richly-embroidered dresses had a design of cockleshells — some of the more dour and gloomy courtiers at the royal court of Mary, Queen of Scots said she was a very contrary lady.

The Queen also had four loyal serving ladies of whom she was very fond: Like the Queen they, too, were all called Mary, and perhaps they were the pretty maids mentioned in the rhyme.

MISS MUFFET

Another little girl who found fame in a rhyme was Patience Muffet, whose father

CLEVER JACK HORNER

was very interested in the study of spiders and other small insects. But we do not really know if Patience was not very fond of spiders or if she enjoyed eating curds and whey. Perhaps, like you, she much preferred sweets and chocolate!

MARY'S LAMB

Everyone knows the story of Mary, who had a little lamb which followed her each day to school. There was a real little girl called Mary Sawyer whose pet lamb followed her to the schoolhouse at Sudbury in Massachusetts in the United States, and there are a collection of documents which prove that she is the person around whom the familiar rhyme is written.

Some people believe that the real Jack Horner lived in the days of King Henry the Eighth, who was always pleased to receive presents.

The Master Horner mentioned in the rhyme was the servant of the Abbot of Glastonbury who, wishing to please the king, sent Master Horner with a very special pie to the palace.

It was Christmas time, and on the long journey through the snow Jack opened up the pie and found in it the title deeds to twelve fine manor houses. He decided that the king would not miss one, and so he selected a fine manor house in Somerset for himself.

Clever Master Hunter had picked himself a fine 'plum' indeed from *that* Christmas pie!

LADYBIRD-LADYBIRD

THE STORY OF
THE NURSERY RHYME

Mrs. Ladybird opened her wings and flew quietly down to the town, holding her shopping basket in one hand and her red umbrella in the other, because it looked as though it was going to rain.

First she went into the butcher's shop and bought some nice pork chops and a packet of sage and onion stuffing.

Then she went into the greengrocer's shop and bought some apples and pears and a large bunch of purple grapes.

She had a very big family and they always seemed to be hungry, so her next visit was to the dairy, where she bought some butter and cheese, and one dozen eggs and a pot of cream.

Her shopping basket was getting rather full, so she just popped into the sweet shop to buy a packet of toffees, and some chocolate peppermint creams, and then she started to fly back to her home, which was on a large bush of yellow broom, in a little garden near the railway.

She had only gone a little way when

she suddenly realised she had her shopping basket in one hand, but nothing in the other! She must have left her umbrella behind.

Back she flew, as fast as her wings would take her, and went into the butcher's shop.

"Excuse me, but have you seen my red umbrella?" she asked politely.

"Red umbrella, Madam? Oh no, I don't sell umbrellas. I sell pork chops and Canterbury lamb, but I don't sell umbrellas. Red, black, or any other colour!"

"So sorry to have troubled you," said Mrs. Ladybird, and she went next door to the greengrocer.

"Excuse me, but have you seen my red umbrella?"

"Red umbrella?" said the greengrocer rather crossly, because he'd just dropped a big potato on his toe. "Have I seen a red umbrella? Good gracious, no! I can see a red apple, and a red tomato, and a red beetroot, but even with my spectacles on I can't see a red umbrella anywhere."

"So sorry to have troubled you,"

said Mrs. Ladybird, and then she went into the dairy.

"Excuse me, but have you seen my red umbrella?"

"Red umbrella, my dear," said the dairy lady kindly. "Oh no, there've been no umbrellas left in my shop. People sometimes leave their gloves or their baskets behind, but I haven't seen any umbrellas. I only wish I could help you, my dear."

"Thank you so much," said Mrs. Ladybird, as she went sadly out of the shop. "I'm sorry to have troubled you."

She stood outside on the pavement, wondering what to do, and just then it began to rain. First a few little drops, and then faster and faster until it was pouring down and poor Mrs. Ladybird thought it would wash the little black spots off her shiny red back!

Then she remembered the sweet shop. Perhaps that was where she had left her umbrella. Skipping over the puddles she popped inside, and there, lying on the counter, was a red umbrella.

She was so glad to see it again, and she thanked the sweet-shop lady for looking after it for her. "I was beginning to think I had lost it for ever," she said, in quite a tearful voice.

Mrs. Ladybird picked up her shopping basket and flew off home as fast as her wings would take her, holding her umbrella over her head to keep off the rain.

When she reached the large bush of yellow broom she found everyone in a terrible state. A spark from a passing train had set fire to the bank near the little garden, and all Mrs. Ladybird's children had flown out of the broom bush and settled on a rose tree in the next garden.

Luckily, the lady who lived in the cottage came running out and quickly put out the fire, and the bush of yellow broom was quite safe.

At first Mrs. Ladybird couldn't find her children anywhere. But when they smelt the nice pork chops she was cooking they soon came flying home again. While they were eating their dinner they told her all about the fire, and she told them all about her search for her dear little red umbrella.

Animal ABC

A is for antelope,
How far does he roam
Across the plains and the jungles
Of his African home?

B is for baboon,
He's often seen
At the zoo—but don't touch him,
He's sullen and mean.

C is for camel,
In the hump that he's got
On his back he stores water,
So he's cool when it's hot.

D is for duck
And also for drake,
They peacefully swim
On the silvery lake.

E is for elephant;
Look at the size
Of his trunk as he bellows
His trumpeting cries.

F is for fox,
He'll soon try to catch
One of the chickens
If the door's off the latch.

126

H is for hippopotamus,
He's called River Horse;
But though he's good-natured
You can't ride him, of course.

G is for gorilla,
If put in a cage
He'll beat on his chest
And give loud roars of rage.

I is for ibex,
Who lives in the deep
Snows of the Alps
And from rock to rock leaps.

J is for jaguar,
His eyes are so bright
As he hungrily prowls
Through the jungle at night.

K is for koala,
She's soft and she's warm,
Her young one clings tight
So he'll come to no harm.

L is for lion,
From under his mane
He proudly stares out
At his kingdom the plain.

M is for the little
Blind velvety mole
Who sleeps through the winter
In his underground hole.

N is for Neddy,
A little donkey who
Spends his summer on the sands,
Will he give a ride to you?

O is for otter,
He's chasing after fish.
When he catches them he eats them—
They're his favourite dish.

P is for Panda,
He's coloured black and white,
But although he looks pleasant
He can certainly bite.

Q is for quagga,
I think it would be true
To say he looked a lot like
Someone else, don't you?

R is for rhino,
He's got one very large
Horn, if he scents you
He'll probably charge.

132

S is for seal.
A great big fish,
He wouldn't fit
On any dish.

T is for Tiger,
He prowls the forest at night,
If you hear him roar
It will give you a fright.

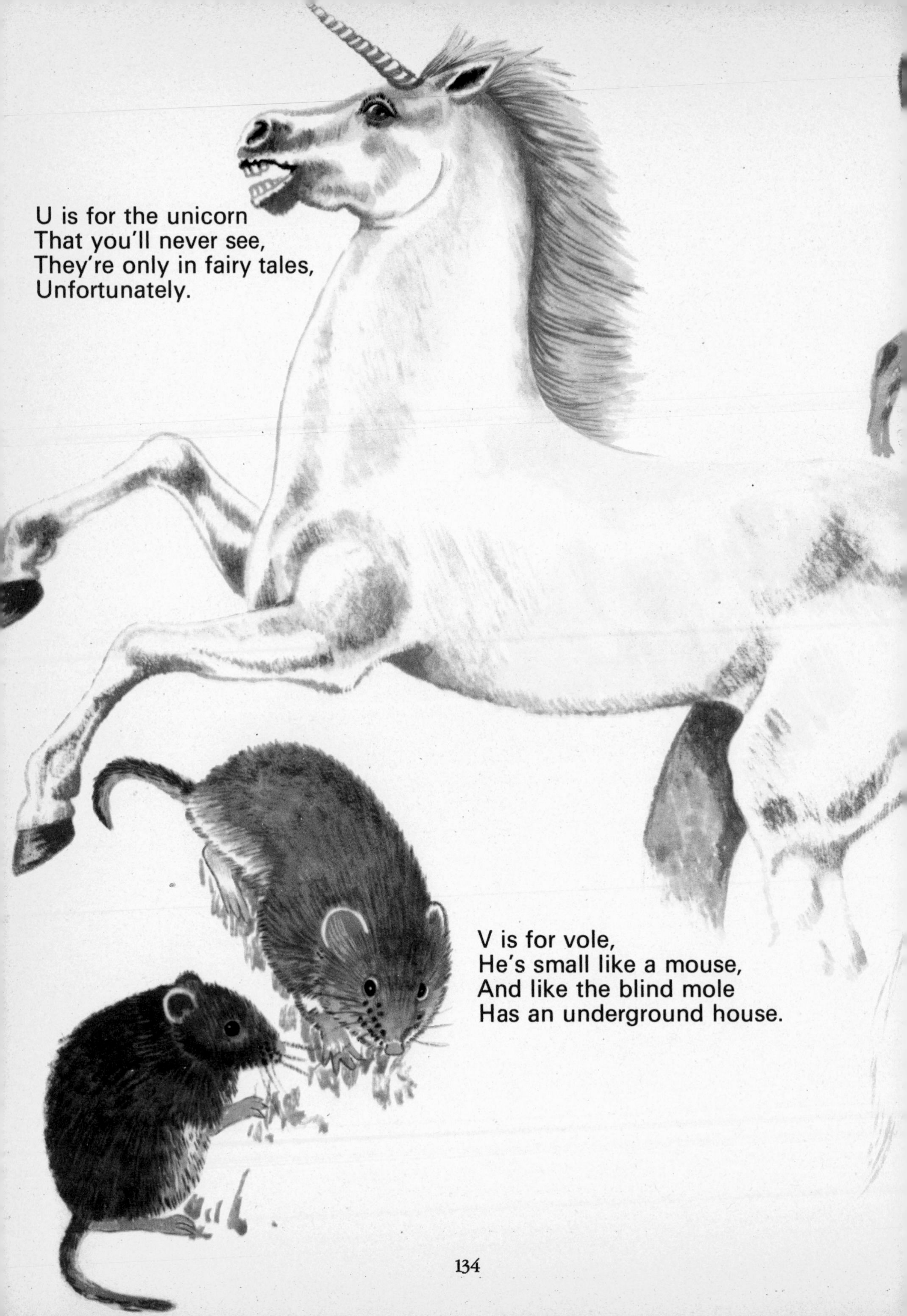

U is for the unicorn
That you'll never see,
They're only in fairy tales,
Unfortunately.

V is for vole,
He's small like a mouse,
And like the blind mole
Has an underground house.

W is for wart-hog,
He's got short, bristly hair,
And runs through the forest
With his tail up in the air.

X finishes lynx,
I hope this will do,
For I can't think of a beast
That starts with X —can you?

Y is for yak,
See him carry his load
On his broad-shouldered back
Up the cold mountain road.

Z is for zebra,
He's happy and gay,
But he's last in the alphabet,
I'm sorry to say.

Mary...Mary

Mary had a little lamb,
Its fleece was white as snow,
And everywhere that Mary went
The lamb was sure to go.

It followed her to school one day:
That was against the rule;
It made the children laugh and play
To see the lamb at school.

"What makes the lamb love Mary so?"
The eager children cry.
"Why, Mary loves the lamb, you see,"
The teacher did reply.

Mary had a pretty bird,
Feathers bright and yellow;
Slender legs, upon my word,
He was a pretty fellow.

The sweetest notes he always sang,
Which much delighted Mary;
And near the cage she'd ever sit,
To hear her own canary.

Mistress Mary, quite contrary,
How does your garden grow?
With silver bells and cockle shells
And pretty maids all in a row.

COTTONWOOL LAMBS and SWEETMEAT PIGS

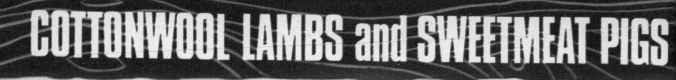

Some children are puzzled by the familiar nursery rhyme which tells of Tom the piper's son being smacked for stealing and later *eating* a pig.

This is because the rhyme is usually illustrated with a picture of naughty Tom running away with a fat, squealing pig. But the pig which the boy stole and which inspired the rhyme was not a live pig at all, but a sweetmeat one, with a coat of currant buttons and two currant buttons for its eyes.

These pig models, usually made from gingerbread or shortbread or a similar sweetmeat, were sold by hawkers in the streets of London long ago.

The seller often advertised his wares with this less familiar nursery rhyme:

A long tail'd pig,
Or a short tail'd pig,
Or a pig without any tail,
A boar pig, or a sow pig,
Or a pig with a curly tail.
Take hold of its tail and eat of its head;
For this is a pig made from sweet gingerbread.

Another familiar street cry of about the same time was:

Young lambs to sell! Young lambs to sell!
I never would cry young lambs to sell
If I'd as much money as I could tell,
I never would cry young lambs to sell.
Dolly and Molly, Richard and Nell,
Buy my young lambs and I'll use you well.

These lambs were usually sold by wounded soldiers who had returned home from the wars and who used their clever fingers to earn a living.

The lambs were made in cotton wool and had gilt spangles among their fleece. Their horns and legs were made from tin to make them sturdy enough to play with, and they had gay little collars, made from bright-pink tape, fastened around their neck. Their heads were made from paste and very skilfully moulded to the fleeces.

They were very popular playthings and a seller was sure to empty his tray very quickly once the children knew he was there . . . for these enchanting little creatures cost only one penny!

a stable secret

HORACE was Farmer Kendal's best cart horse. He was big and strong and had lots of thick hair round each hoof.

Horace was secretly rather proud of his sturdy legs, but his nice honest grey face would have blushed for shame if the other horses had known it.

One spring day Horace woke up early and rolled over on the stable straw to talk to his friend Winkle, who was Farmer Kendal's second best horse.

Winkle raised his head, sniffing the air. "It smells uncommonly like ploughing time, Horace, old boy," he said. "We

141

shall be pulling the old plough together any day now, you mark my words."

Horace shook his thick grey mane and whinnied excitedly. He loved hard work, especially ploughing.

They stood side by side and looked out over the open top of the stable door. The white mists began to roll up the fields from the river, and the rooks chattered in the tree tops as if they felt something new in the air.

"Look at the flock of little white gulls," said Horace. "They know it's time for ploughing, the greedy rascals, they're waiting to follow us as we turn up the furrows."

Jack, the farmer's boy, came clattering through the yard to open the stable doors.

"Morning, Jack," whinnied Horace. "We're going to start ploughing, aren't we? I knew we were. Hurray!"

He kicked up his stout legs and danced clumsily over the cobbles. Winkle followed him, tossing his mane and stamping his feet.

"Steady, me lads, steady!" cried Jack. He could not understand a word they were saying, but he knew they were excited about something.

The two friends expected to be harnessed to the plough at once and were surprised when Jack left them in the paddock.

Winkle began to crop the short grass while Horace watched Jack striding down the lane. But he was suddenly startled to hear a strange noise.

"I say, Winkle, come here. Look at this queer beast running down the lane. What can it be?"

"It makes a queer kind of a noise," said Winkle, pressing up against Horace. He was not quite as brave as his friend.

"I don't like the colour of its coat," said Horace firmly. "And, just fancy, master is riding on its back," he added, as the queer beast drew near.

The farmer and his two men seemed very pleased with the strange new creature. They stroked its shining coat and thumped its peculiar legs.

Winkle and Horace snorted in disgust.

"It smells awful!" said Winkle, wrinkling his nose. "I wonder what it eats? I can't see anything like a mouth."

Horace shook his head in wonderment. "I hope they don't stable it with me," he said, turning his back as if he never wished to look at it again.

Suddenly Winkle groaned and sat down with a bump as if he had received a dreadful shock.

"Oh, Horace, old fellow, it's plough-ing," he whispered in a voice of misery.

The new animal chugged up and down the field with Jack on its back, leaving behind newly turned furrows of dark earth. The gulls rose from the river bank in a flock and swooped excitedly upon the freshly ploughed furrows.

Winkle dropped his brown head and a tear splashed on the grass. He walked sadly into the stable and hid his face in the straw. Horace felt a hard lump come into his throat, almost choking him with dis-appointment.

It was a very sad day for the two old friends.

When evening came they lay in the stable trying to sleep. But all the time Horace thought of the new rival and wondered whether they would ever be allowed to plough again.

Suddenly there was a gentle tap on the door and a soft voice said: " Hello, you two. Can I come in?"

There was a scraping and a scratching as the latch was lifted, then in walked a strange figure.

" Why, it's old Sam Sleepy, the scare-crow," exclaimed Winkle. " Whatever are you doing here at this time of night?"

Sam Sleepy screwed up his quaint face and winked. " I called to you this after-noon, old fellow-me-lads, but you were too worried to notice me. So here I am. I couldn't come earlier because Farmer Kendal was about. He was busy putting that new tractor to bed."

Horace remembered his troubles and groaned. " So it's called a tractor, is it? Well, I don't like that for a name. And it hasn't even one leg, nor a face, nor a tail,

nor any nice bushy whiskers on its feet like me."

Sammy Sleepy began to laugh. "Cheer up, old thing!" he said. "That's just what I've come to see you about. You're not going to let that red and yellow chugging creature do all your favourite work, are you? Why don't you think of some way to stop it? It hasn't half the brains you have, Horace. Why it can't even *eat*. It drinks nothing but horrible smelly petrol out of tins."

Horace and Winkle began to cheer up. Horace was pleased to hear he had brains.

"Come on," he said boldly, standing up for the first time that day to his full height. He shook his mane and strode out of the barn into the darkness, followed by faithful Winkle and Sam Sleepy. The moon slid from the back of a cloud and bathed the fields with soft light as they tiptoed under the shadowy trees so that no one but the owls should see them.

Under an old tin roof near the barn stood the tractor. By its side were several tins of petrol.

"Look," whispered Sam, "this is what it drinks. Doesn't it smell terrible?"

Horace pulled a face and **shuddered**. Then, in the twinkling of an eye, he swept all the petrol tins over with his heavy fore legs and trampled on them.

Sam Sleepy waved his strawstuffed arms and jumped up and down, saying: "Good old Horace. Good old Horace!"

Winkle began to giggle. "If it has nothing to drink," he said, "it won't feel much like work, will it?"

He marched boldly up to the tractor and gave it a hearty kick. There was a queer little rattling noise inside the engine, then all was still.

"I knew you could do it. I knew you could! Good for you, boys!" chuckled Sam, who was not as sleepy as people thought.

Horace and Winkle trotted back to the stable feeling much better. They thanked their friend for his advice.

"It was awfully good of you, Sam, to come all that way over the fields just to help us," said Horace.

"Oh, no trouble at all, boys," murmured Sam, waving a ragged arm. "Bye, bye. See you in the morning."

He stumped off to his duties once more while the horses settled down in the straw. They fell asleep at once.

Next morning there was a terrible rumpus. Farmer Kendal and the two men stood over the battered tractor and the empty petrol tins and argued loud and long, making so much noise that they woke the horses.

"Come on, Winkle," said Horace cheerfully, "get yourself in working order, we shall be wanted today."

The two conspirators flexed their muscles vigorously.

From the distance came an angry voice thundering: "Who has done all this damage?"

And an old brown owl flying home after a night's hunting called mockingly: "Who? Who?"

A little later Sam Sleepy watched Horace and Winkle at work with the plough. Their heads were held high, the sun glistened on their harness, and the wind ruffled the whiskers on Horace's hard-working legs.

It was a beautiful day.

As they reached the top of the field they looked across at Sam. Then three eyelids winked knowingly. One was Sam's, one was Winkle's, and the third belonged to clever Horace.

AS
I WAS
GOING...

As I was going to Derby,
Upon a market day,
I met the finest ram, sir,
That ever was fed on hay.

As I was going to St. Ives,
I met a man with seven wives,
Each wife had seven sacks,
Each sack had seven cats,
Each cat had seven kits:
Kits, cats, sacks and wives,
How many were going to St. Ives?

As I was going up Primrose Hill,
Primrose Hill was dirty;
There I met a pretty miss,
And she dropped me a curtsey.

As I was going to Banbury,
Upon a summer's day,
My dame had butter, eggs, and fruit,
And I had corn and hay;
Joe drove the ox, and Tom the swine,
Dick took the foal and mare,
I sold them all—then home to dine,
From famous Banbury Fair.

148

Harvest Home

"My dear!" said Harvest Mouse to her neighbour the shrew, "whatever is the *Bururururururrrrring* noise we can hear?"

"Don't you know?" panted the Shrew Mouse. "I heard it last year."

"But I'm a *this*-year's mouse. I haven't heard it before," said Harvest Mouse. "And I don't like it!"

"Neither do I," said Shrew Mouse, "we shall have to go, and quickly, to new homes. *That* is the reaper, cutting the corn."

"But—but they can't do that!" protested Harvest Mouse. "*We* live here!"

"*BURURURURRRRRRR!*" The noise was coming very close.

"We shall have to go. NOW!" called Shrew Mouse. "Come quickly. Follow me."

Together they ran further into the cornfield, away from the circling harvest machine. Together they huddled among the corn stalks, and presently Harvest Mouse, overcome by curiosity, climbed up one of them. The reaper was not far away.

Each day during the next few days they ran together further into the centre of the field, until at length there remained only about an acre of corn to be cut.

"I expect they'll finish it tonight," said Shrew Mouse. "They'll have to, before any more rain comes."

But, to their surprise, the big shire horse drawing the reaper stopped. The farm man jumped down. "I'm tired," he said, "and it's getting dark. We can't see to go round these hillocks, Bob, we'll go home."

Bob, the big shire, nodded in agreement, and put his nose down into the cut corn, to pick up a few straws. In fact, he nearly picked up tiny Harvest Mouse and Shrew, who were sheltering almost beneath his feet.

"SQUEEEEEE!" yelled Harvest

Mouse, and Bob indignantly lifted his head high in the air and backed a few paces.

"WHOA THERE!" called the farm man, and Bob stopped.

Bob and Harvest Mouse stood staring at each other. Harvest Mouse could hardly believe in such a large giant.

Bob smiled. "All right," he said, "You did startle me, but I don't eat mice. Don't be frightened, I'm very gentle, really." He turned and looked at the standing corn. "But you'll have to run away from here . . . ."

Before he could say any more the farm man came and unbuckled his harness and led him away.

"I've got an idea," said Harvest Mouse, "follow me."

Next morning the rain came down in torrents, and no work was done in the field for a week. But Harvest Mouse and her friend didn't worry. They had found a shelter in the farm cart in the middle of the cornfield. Towards the middle of the second week the dried corn was taken to the farm-yard, and Harvest Mouse and her friend jumped down from the cart and began to explore.

The hens clucked at them and drove them away; the pig threatened to eat them up; the bull nearly trod on them; Dorothy Duck almost made a meal of them; Farmyard Cat chased them; in fact they created such a hullabaloo that the farmer's wife came out to see, and she had a carving knife in her hand!

"WHEEEEE!" yelled the two mice and darted under a door into . . . . the stable. There, gently pulling hay from the manger, stood Bob.

"My dears," said Bob, "don't be frightened. I don't eat mice. Would you like to stay here till the harvest is home?"

Thankfully they settled in the manger.

THE DREAM

Last night I had a dream, and it was so very strange,
I thought I was a cowboy a-riding on the range,
And then my dream did change.

I was then an Arab leader on a horse with a snow-white mane,
Fighting all the soldiers on a golden desert plain,
And just as I was winning, my dream did change again.

This time I was a hunter, a-rowing on a lake,
And later in the jungle I met a great big snake,
And when it nearly caught me —was I glad that I did wake!

THE KING WHO COULD NOT WAKE UP

It was ten o'clock on the morning of Princess Cherry-Blossom's wedding day. From early morning the villagers and townsfolk from far and near had been lining the road from the palace to see their lovely princess drive away with her handsome prince to his castle beyond the river.

Within the palace, however, all was not well. Servants and courtiers hurried to and fro through the endless passages, the princess was weeping, and the queen sent for first one and then another of the wise men of the court, to seek their help.

The evening before, the king and queen had given a royal ball in honour of the princess. But just as the fiddlers had struck up a merry tune for the dancing to begin, a great hush had fallen over the ballroom, and all eyes had turned towards the king.

Slumped back in the royal chair, with his crown pushed sideways, the king was fast asleep, and from the royal nose there came again and again, like a warning foghorn, a deep and ugly snore.

The queen had tapped his face with her fan, calling softly to him to wake up, but the snores only grew louder.

Until the king had led his partner onto the dance floor, no one else could dance, and so, one by one, the guests had bowed and curtsied to the queen, and hurried away from the royal palace.

The court doctors were summoned, the cooks, and the serving men, but no one could tell the cause of this strange sleep. No wine, no food, no fruit nor perfume could be traced that might explain it, and everyone was in despair.

Six servants carried His Majesty to the royal bedchamber where, through all the hours of darkness, the snoring continued steadily. Daylight came, the morning of the princess's wedding day, but still there was no change.

At the queen's command, the wise men of the court put their heads together, searching for a cure. Ice was placed on the king's forehead. A page-boy stood by his head clanging a bell, which echoed through the corridors, while another tickled the soles of his feet with a peacock's feather. An onion was dangled before the royal nose, which brought tears streaming down the cheeks. Two servants even lifted the king to his feet, and supported him, but nothing could stop the snoring, or bring even a flutter to the royal eyelids.

The news spread fast through the waiting crowds, and soon an old man was seen hobbling through the gates of the royal palace. Under his arm he carried a thick book. A few words with the palace guards, and he was at once permitted to enter through the great oak doors, and shown into the presence of the queen. He bowed low.

"Your Majesty," he began. "I bring you grave news. The king is under the power of a spell, the Sleeping Spell. No one will have power to waken him until the spell is broken."

A cry of dismay broke from the lips of the courtiers.

"Who could have done such a thing?" they asked each other. "Who could wish to harm the king or stop the wedding of our beloved princess?"

"It doesn't matter now who it was," cried the queen. "Just tell me, old man, how can the spell be broken?"

The old man began to thumb through his book, muttering to himself as he did so: "Sneezing – no. Shouting – no. Singing, sobbing, – ah, yes. Here it is – sleeping. How to break the Sleeping Spell."

The queen and all the courtiers waited anxiously as the old man studied his book. At last he spoke.

"Your Majesty," he declared, "it will not be easy. You will need a wild singing bird to enchant the royal ears, the juice of the red berries that grow on the highest mountain slopes to moisten the royal lips, and a lock of hair from the head of the one who has cast the spell."

"Alas, alas," moaned the courtiers. "How can these be found in time? Indeed, we do not even know who cast the spell!"

"Found they must be," declared the queen bravely. "Let it be known that a hundred pieces of gold will be the reward to anyone who can help to break the spell in time for the wedding."

Then all was hustle and bustle. The crowds by the palace gates soon hurried away, everyone anxious to win a share of the promised gold. Only a few old women waited; too old to join the search, they lingered by the palace gates, determined not to miss any of the excitement.

Time was passing all too quickly, but at last a child came hurrying through the gates and entered the palace. When she was shown into the presence of the queen, she took from the folds of her shawl a little brown lark she had caught on the hillside.

"A wild singing bird to enchant the royal ears, Your Majesty," murmured the child, curtsying to the floor.

Her gift was gladly received, and the queen commanded that the child should be rewarded with her share of the promised gold.

A long time passed, and then a cheer went up from a group of palace servants as a young man hurried through the gates, his clothes torn, his face scratched and bleeding, and his boots heavy with mud. In his hand he carried a spray of the precious red berries from the high mountain slopes. He, too, received his reward.

"Now there remains the hardest of

them all," declared the old man, as he turned again through the pages of his book. "Is there no one who can tell who might have cast this spell?"

Suddenly one of the courtiers clapped his hands excitedly. "Of course," he cried. "The old woodcutter from the hut many miles beyond the river. When the king and his party were out hunting yesterday morning, the woodcutter was splashed with mud as the horses galloped by. He shouted angrily after the king as he passed. It must have been he who cast the spell."

"Alas," cried the courtiers. "How-

ever can anyone ride so far and be back in time for the wedding? Why, it would be dusk before anyone could complete such a journey."

"The journey must be done," ordered the queen. "We must not fail now, and the reward to him who brings the lock of hair will be not one hundred, but five hundred pieces of gold."

Then the great hunt started. Men sprang to their saddles and spurred their horses to a furious gallop, each eager to win the reward. From the palace rooftop servants watched as the tiny figures raced away in the distance.

More and more people were gathering by the palace gates as the hour of the wedding drew near. Only the strong young men had taken part in this last difficult search, and the old men and the old women shook their heads in despair as time passed and still the king slept on.

All hope was fading when a young stable boy came hurrying to the palace, carrying a basket.

"My brother bade me bring this to the queen," he explained. "When he rode away in search of the lock of hair, he took with him his prize homing pigeon, knowing that no horse in the land could match its swift return. Here, ringed to its leg," he said, opening the lid of the basket, "is the lock of hair which can break the spell."

Then there arose a great cheering and rejoicing, which echoed through the palace, with cries of "The spell is broken. The king is awake."

In the streets the people laughed and danced with delight that the wedding of their princess could now take place. And, high above the palace, there fluttered, unnoticed, a small brown bird, carolling its own sweet song of joy for the princess's happiness.

Skip and Hop

Once upon a day-dream,
In a place called Windy Top,
There lived two merry squirrels,
Their names were Skip and Hop.

Their home was in the branches
Of a tall and leafy tree,
And they worked all day together
Making boats to sail the sea.

The boats were made from nut-shells,
Very small, but oh so strong,
So that when they sailed the ocean
They would bob and dance along.

For Hop would gather oak-leaves,
Which he made into a sail,
And fastened them upon the boat
With hammer and with nail.

Then Skip would dip his paint-brush
In the blue-bells growing nigh,
And paint the boats the colour
Of the sunny summer sky.

And when their work was finished,
All the fairies from the glade,
Would call to see the nut-shell boats,
Which Skip and Hop had made.

The Enchanted Flower

ROSSE was a young woodcutter who lived alone in a small cottage in the forest. Every day he went out felling trees, and every night he came home to his little cottage and made his supper.

One night he cooked a pancake and sat eating it.

" Oh dear," sighed Rosse, " I'm so tired, but I shall have to clean this kitchen up before I go to bed. Pots to wash, the floor to sweep and everything to dust." Wearily he set to work.

The next day Rosse was up early, for he had a long walk before his work began.

It was a beautiful spring morning. The birds were singing and the forest was carpeted with bluebells.

As he walked along the narrow paths he suddenly noticed a flash of deep pink in the carpet of blue. Curiosity made him pause to look again.

" That's a pretty flower," murmured Rosse. " I wonder what it is?" He stooped and plucked it. " What a beautiful scent it has," he thought, and he slipped it into his buttonhole.

All day he worked hard felling trees, and when his work was done he set off on the long walk home.

As he slipped on his coat he noticed the little flower.

"Why," he thought, "it looks as fresh as it did this morning."

When Rosse got home he popped the flower carefully into a little pot of water before he had his supper. By the time he had eaten, fed his dog and hens, and chopped some wood for morning, it was bedtime. He decided to leave the washing-up and sweeping until the morning.

The following day he was up with the lark.

"I must clean my cottage before I go out this morning," he said to his dog Rex as he dressed.

But when he entered the little kitchen he could hardly believe his eyes. The table was laid, his bacon was sizzling in the pan and the kettle just on the boil. The floor was swept and everything was tidied and dusted.

"Well," gasped Rosse, "whatever has happened?"

Rex looked up, sniffed the air, and wagged his tail.

"Would you believe it?" laughed Rosse, "we've a nice breakfast all ready for us. Let's eat it old chap."

When they had finished, Rosse cleared the table and put the little pot with the flower in it on the windowsill. Then, shouldering his axe, he called Rex and they set off.

When he arrived home that night the same thing had happened. A meal was ready on the table and the cottage was beautifully clean.

"It is very strange, Rex," said Rosse, patting the faithful dog who gazed at him. "I locked the door this morning, and no one could have broken in without my knowing. Yet everything is spick and span as though someone has worked here all day. I wish I knew who it was."

Day after day the cottage was kept clean and tidy, although Rosse always locked the door when he went out and there wasn't another cottage for miles.

At last Rosse could stand it no longer.

" I must find out who does it," he cried to Rex, as they walked home through the forest. " I'll go now and visit the Wise Woman of the Wood. She might be able to tell me."

So instead of going straight home he turned up another path, and soon reached the queer little house of the Wise Woman.

" Come in," called a shrill voice, and Rosse entered a strange little room, full of charms and stuffed animals and birds.

Quickly Rosse told the Wise Woman what had happened in his cottage.

She smiled and nodded. " I see, I see," she murmured. " You want to know who does the work for you?"

" Indeed I do," cried Rosse, " if only so that I can thank them."

" Well," nodded the Wise Woman, " you must go to bed as usual tonight, but don't sleep. As soon as the clock says five

minutes to twelve creep downstairs with a sheet in your hands."

"A sheet," repeated Rosse, looking puzzled.

"Don't interrupt," said the Wise Woman sternly. "When you peep round the kitchen door you must be ready to throw the sheet over the first thing you see moving."

Rosse was very puzzled, but the Wise Woman would tell him no more, so he thanked her and went home.

That night at ten o'clock, he and Rex went upstairs. Rex always slept on a mat in his master's bedroom.

"We mustn't go to sleep old chap," whispered Rosse, and Rex wagged his tail and seemed to understand.

It was a long time to wait, not making a sound, but at last the clock hands stood at five minutes to twelve.

Rosse, clutching the sheet, crept softly down the stairs. The moon was up and shining brightly, so that when he reached the kitchen it was as bright as day.

Rosse stood there, peeping round the door which stood ajar. The room was empty and not a sound was to be heard.

But suddenly Rosse's eyes nearly popped out of his head. For the first thing to move was the little pink flower! It flopped out of the pot on to the floor. Quickly Rosse sprang in and dropped the sheet over it.

The sheet seemed to rise, and fall, and rise again.

Rosse, trembling, put out a hand and whisked it aside, and there before him stood a beautiful maiden!

"W-w-why, who are you?" he stammered.

The maiden smiled. "I am Campion," she replied, "and I was enchanted by a wicked fairy. I was doomed to remain a flower until a human being should care for me. When you plucked me

the spell was partly broken so that I was able to return to my own shape whenever I was alone."

"Then *you* have kept my cottage so beautiful all these days?" gasped Rosse.

"Yes," nodded Campion, "and now you have broken the spell completely. How did you find out what to do?"

"I went to the Wise Woman of the Woods," answered Rosse, "because I wanted to thank whoever was looking after me so well."

Campion gave him her hand. "How can I ever thank *you*?" she cried. "I owe you more than I can repay."

Rosse looked round the little cottage and down at his faithful dog.

"Mine is a humble home," he faltered at last, "but I should be happy as a king if only you would share it with me."

So Campion stayed with him and they were happy as the days were long.

"How glad I am I stopped to pluck that little flower," Rosse would say to Rex as they walked through the forest. "Who would have dreamed it would bring me such happiness?"

And Rex would bark and wag his tail, just as though he understood.

Journey to Fairyland

I am sure you all know the nursery rhyme about the lion and the unicorn fighting for the crown — but have you ever seen a unicorn? There are always plenty of lions in the zoo or roaming freely in the jungle, but no one has ever seen a unicorn.

I will let you into a little secret and tell you why. Unicorns are special little fairy creatures who, because mortals laughed when the king of the unicorns lost his battle against the lion, ran away to fairyland, where the fairies welcomed them warmly.

The Fairy Queen thought the unicorn a delightful animal, with its bright blue eyes, and the one golden horn in the middle of its head. She asked the unicorns to draw her golden coach on important occasions. The unicorns were very honoured to be asked to do this and they happily agreed, for they liked living in fairyland.

But mortal people were very puzzled and sorry when they no longer saw the unicorns, for they believed that the unicorn's horn had magic properties. If it touched muddy water it made the water pure again immediately, and if anyone was lucky enough to get close enough to touch a unicorn's horn, that person was given the choice of becoming rich, beautiful or wise.

The king of the unicorns also missed roaming the green pastures of the earth. So, at last, the Fairy Queen said that for one day of the year he should return to earth and search for the kindest child. As a reward for his goodness this child should be brought back to fairyland on Midsummer's Eve to join in the fairy revels on the most important night of the year for all fairy folk.

The lucky child is always returned to his bed before dawn, and he always promises never to reveal where he has been. But, just to make sure that no mortals ever enter fairyland un-invited, before leaving the house the unicorn always touches the door with his magic horn. This weaves a spell around the house and when the child wakes in the morning he firmly believes that all his adventures of the night before were just a wonderful dream.

So always try to be good and kind and, who knows, perhaps this year it will be *your* turn to ride on the back of a unicorn on a magic journey to fairyland.

SIMPLE SIMON

A TALE FROM THE NURSERY RHYME

Once a year, on May Day, a fair came to Nursery Rhyme Land, and for everyone it was a day for fun and merriment. No one enjoyed the fair more than Simple Simon, who lived with his mother in a tiny, tumbledown cottage down by Buttercup Meadow.

Simon was a kind-hearted boy, but he really was so silly that he believed everything that anyone told him, and because of this, some of the naughtier and more mischievous Nursery Rhyme folk were able to play tricks on him.

Naughty Jack Horner told Simon that if he fished in his mother's washing pail, Simon might be lucky enough to catch a whale. Simon sat all morning patiently fishing until his mother came to find him at lunch time.

"Oh, Simon," she cried, shaking her head ruefully, "whales live in the ocean. You will never catch one in a bucket. Jack Horner can always play jokes on you. You really ought not to listen to anything he says. Don't you remember how he persuaded you to try some honey he had made . . . and it was really very hot mustard?"

"Yes, it burnt my tongue dreadfully," admitted Simon, wryly. "And Boy Blue persuaded me to climb up a tree to look at a bird's nest yesterday."

"And the bough broke and you fell into a muddy pool beneath the tree," said his mother sadly.

"Yes, but Jill took me home and her mother gave me some of Jack's clothes to wear until mine dried out," said Simon with a grin. "Jill's mother said that she is used to accidents with her own two children."

"I can imagine that," replied Simon's mother, thinking of the many times Jack and Jill had fallen and got soaked carrying their pail of water down the hill. "But do try and think before you act in future, Simon, and then people won't keep telling me what

169

a simple little boy you are."

"Very well, mother," replied Simon, cheerfully. "How much money can you spare to give me for the fair tomorrow?"

"If you will deliver these three bundles of washing to Bobby Shaftoe, Gregory Griggs and Peter Piper, I will give you three silver pennies. But do take care, Simon, the washing is clean, and I don't want you to drop any in the mud."

"You need have no fear, mother, I shall earn those three silver pennies," laughed Simon, as he picked up the bundles of washing and set off.

And, to his great delight, not only did he deliver the washing safely but Bobby, Gregory and Peter each gave him a silver penny for being such a smart errand boy.

"Now I shall have six pennies to spend at the fair," cried Simon happily as he went off to bed that night.

The day of the fair dawned bright and clear, and when Jack and Jill and Tom, the piper's son, called for Simon, he was ready, swinging on the garden gate, awaiting their arrival.

"Now, Simon, don't do anything silly," warned his mother, as she waved them all off. "Take care of your money and have a good time."

"Don't worry, we will look after

him," cried Jack and Jill, as they waved gaily to Simon's mother.

On the way they met Jack Horner and Boy Blue, who were also going to the fair.

"Hello, Simon," cried Jack Horner, a naughty twinkle in his eye. "Did you know that those thistles over there are full of ripe plums?"

"Are they?" cried Simon eagerly. "I love plums. I will pick some for us all."

"Wait, Simon, Jack is only joking," cried Tom.

But he spoke too late, for Simon had already seized a handful of thistles, expecting to find them full of plums.

"Oh, my poor hands," he cried as the thistles pricked him badly. He opened his hands to let the thistles drop . . . and his precious silver pennies rolled away into the deep ditch by the side of the road.

"Oh, Jack Horner, that really was too bad of you!" cried Jill, crossly. "We can't get the money back because the ditch is too deep, and it's also full of thistles. Now Simon won't have any money to spend at the fair."

"That's a pity, but he shouldn't be so silly," cried naughty Jack. But he looked very ashamed of himself as he and Boy Blue ran off, leaving the others to follow at a slower pace.

"Cheer up, Simon, we will share our money with you," comforted his three friends. "We have still got enough money to all go on the swings and roundabouts."

"It is very kind of you, but I would rather you spent your money on yourselves," replied Simon. "I think this last trick of Jack Horner's has really taught me a lesson. I shall never be so foolish again."

"Then at least some good has come out of that naughty trick," cried Tom. "Oh, look, here comes the pieman on his way to the fair. Good morning, pieman, may we taste your pies?"

"Yes, if you all have a penny," laughed the pieman merrily. "Where is your penny, Simon?"

"I lost my money in the ditch," replied Simon, looking longingly at the hot, tasty pies.

"That was a silly thing to do," said the pieman gravely. But when Jack and Jill told him the whole story he put a kind hand on Simon's shoulder and added gently: "I'm sorry, Simon, it was a horrid trick to play, and I shall tell Mrs. Horner to give Jack a good scolding when next I see her."

Then, suddenly, his bright eyes began to twinkle, as he got an idea. "You say you will not be silly and stupid any more, Simon, so I will give you a chance to do me a good turn . . . and earn yourself some money to spend at the fair. Would you like that?"

Simon nodded eagerly and asked: "What do you want me to do?"

"Well," began the pieman, "the King has asked me to make him a

special singing pie today. I can't tell you any more about it because it is a secret," he said hastily as Simon and his friends gazed at the pieman in astonishment. "But I also have these pies to sell at the fair. Now, Simon, if you sell the pies for me at the fair, you may take half of the money you get for them for yourself. What do you say?"

Simon's quick eyes had seen that there were twenty-four pies on the pieman's tray. "If I manage to sell them all I shall earn twelve silver pennies for myself," he thought. "That will be twice the amount of money that I lost."

"I will sell your pies, Mr. Pieman," he said, with a smile.

"Then take my tray and my hat, and fasten my money purse around your waist," replied the pieman.

"You do look smart, Simon," cried Tom, as they all set off once more for the fair. "Here you are, Simon, I will buy your first pie."

He handed Simon a silver penny, which Simon put away carefully in his purse, before handing over the pie.

"I am taking no chances with *this* money," Simon chuckled.

Everyone was most surprised to see Simon selling pies.

"Pies, hot pies! One silver penny! Come and buy!" called Simon, as he stood watching his friends astride three fiery steeds on the roundabouts.

"I'll take two pies, please, Simon," said Old Mother Hubbard, who had called on her way home from seeing her friend Dame Trot. "I always like to visit the fair to sample the pieman's delicious pies, and my old dog Rover loves them too."

"That's three pies gone already," murmured Simon. "And here come a crowd of the children belonging to the old woman who lives in the shoe. I'm sure they will enjoy a pie."

"One dozen pies, please," said the eldest child, politely, holding out twelve silver pennies. "Pies make a pleasant change from broth," he added with a grin, as he distributed the pies to his brothers and sisters.

Simon's next customer was greedy Georgie Porgie who bought three pies, all for himself. As he was cramming the last crumbs into his mouth along came Tommy Tucker to buy two pies for himself and his wife. "I shall have no need to sing for my supper tonight," he said with a smile.

"May we have a pie each, please?" said a trio of voices, and, turning quickly, Simon saw the three little kittens.

"We've lost our mittens again, so our mother will not give us any of her pie," explained Kitty Kitten. "But luckily we each have a silver penny to buy one for ourselves."

"Here you are, little kittens," smiled Simon, who always felt sorry for the way they kept losing their mittens.

"Please, Simon, may I buy your last pie?" asked Jack Horner, looking very ashamed of himself. "And I really am sorry for playing such a horrid trick on you."

"You did me a good turn, Jack," replied Simon cheerfully. "Now that all the pies are sold I can enjoy myself at the fair."

With his share of the pie money, kind-hearted Simon bought lemonade and popcorn for his three friends and took them on the swings.

As they rose high in the air Jack and Jill sang a little rhyme to Simon and Tom:
"Simple Simon met a pieman
Going to the fair;
Said the pieman to Simple Simon:
'Will you sell my ware?'
Said Simple Simon to the pieman:
'Yes, indeed I will!
And at the fair I'll then make merry
With Tom, and Jack and Jill.' "

175

The Little Mountaineer

Once upon a time there lived a little mountaineer named Fritz. He was a jolly little man with round rosy cheeks and white hair. He always wore a little green hat with a red feather in it.

He had travelled all over the world, climbing mountains and acting as a guide to other people who wished to climb. Wherever there was a mountain you could be sure that Fritz had climbed it.

One day, on his travels, he came across a lovely little valley nestling between seven mountains. As soon as he saw the valley Fritz decided that here was the very place where he would like to end his days. He looked at the seven mountains and said, "I shall climb a different mountain every day of the week."

So he went down into the valley and found that there was just one little house for sale. Exactly the kind valley were very friendly folk and they all loved the little mountaineer.

One day, when Fritz had climbed what he called his Sunday mountain—the big one at the far end of the valley—he stood at the top, as always, to admire the view. But suddenly he stared harder, for there, just ahead of him, was a different mountain, one he had never seen before. It was the tallest and most intriguing mountain he had ever seen, with its top disappearing in the clouds.

"What a lovely mountain," sighed Fritz. "However is it that I haven't seen it before? I must climb it—then and only then can I rest content."

He stayed for such a long time gazing in wonder at this strange new mountain that it was quite dark before he reached the valley again, and his friends were worried about him.

Eagerly he told them of this new and wonderful mountain he had seen and how he intended to climb it the very next day.

of house that Fritz had always wanted, with white walls, gaily painted shutters and a little windowbox in front of each window. What is more, from each of the windows Fritz could see in turn the seven mountains which surrounded the valley.

So Fritz settled in the valley and spent his days climbing the seven mountains and his evenings laughing and talking with his friends and neighbours, for the people of the

His friends, however, were dismayed at his news. "It is the magic mountain," they sighed. "It only appears every so often, and always in a different place. Those who have attempted to climb it have never returned."

But all his friends' arguments could not dissuade Fritz from his plan to climb this strange and wonderful mountain. "I cannot rest until I have climbed it," he said.

The next day, instead of setting out to climb his usual Monday mountain, Fritz set off in search of this new mountain he had seen. All day he searched, but he could not find it.

That evening his friends were relieved to see Fritz home again, safe and sound. They tried once more to persuade him to abandon his quest, but he paid no heed and the next day he set out to search again.

Day after day Fritz searched for the magic mountain without success until he had almost given up hope. Then, one day, he rounded a corner of jagged rock and there, right in

front of him, was the mountain he had been searching for. "At last," he cried and eagerly started to climb.

The going was tough, but Fritz was determined to reach the top. Up and up he climbed, higher and higher, till suddenly he was surrounded by clouds. The strange thing was that, instead of being cold and clammy like the mist on top of mountains usually was, they were warm and soft, like a great eiderdown.

At long last Fritz achieved his greatest ambition and reached the top of the magic mountain, but by now he was so far up in the clouds he couldn't even see the lights from the houses in the valley far below him.

Suddenly Fritz felt very tired and he lay down, just where he was, to sleep a while. He hadn't been sleeping long when he felt a light touch on his shoulder. Immediately he sprang to his feet and was amazed to see a beautiful fairy, clad in a shimmering blue gown, standing before him.

"Congratulations, Fritz," she said gently, "you are the first person ever to climb this mountain—many have tried but only *you* have succeeded. Since this is a magic mountain," she went on, "I will grant you your dearest wish."

Fritz thought for a moment. "The thing I like best in all the world," he said, "is to climb mountains. But alas, I fear I shall soon be too old to do so."

"Fear not, my brave little mountaineer," said the fairy, smiling, "for you shall climb the mountains of eternal youth, high up in the sky. Follow me."

So Fritz followed the fairy high, high up to the clouds which stood like great mountains in the sky.

Far below in the valley his friends mourned Fritz. "Another climber lost

in the search for the magic mountain," they sighed.

But Fritz was not lost, as *you* know, and the next time you see the clouds in the sky standing out like great rugged mountains, if you look really, really hard, you might even see Fritz, the little mountaineer, happily climbing away.

LOST & FOUND

Each of these pictures answers one of the questions below, all of which concern things lost or found by nursery rhyme folk.

1. What did little Betty Blue lose?

2. What did Lucy Locket lose?

3. What did the crooked man find?

4. What did Bo-Peep lose?

5. What did little Jack Horner find in his pie?

6. What did Elizabeth, Elspeth, Betsy and Bess find?

7. What did the three little kittens lose?

8. What did the Queen of Hearts lose?

ANSWERS

1. Her holiday shoe. 2. Her pocket. 3. A crooked sixpence; 4. Her sheep;
5. A plum; 6. A nest with five eggs in it; 7. Their mittens; 8. Her tarts.

181

TEN LITTLE FAIRIES

Ten little fairies went out to dine,
One lost her way home, and then there were nine.

Nine little fairies swinging on a gate,
One climbed over it, and then there were eight.

Eight little fairies visiting pixies down in Devon,
One decided to stay there, and then there were seven.

Seven little fairies went to the wood to chop sticks,
One stopped to pick some flowers, and then there were six.

Six little fairies went for honey from the hive,
One stayed just for a chat, and then there were five.

Five little fairies busily polishing the floor,
One went to make the beds, and then there were four.

Four little fairies flying round a tree,
One chased a butterfly, and then there were three.

Three little fairies, all dressed in blue,
One went shopping, and then there were two.

Two little fairies, sad their friends were gone,
One went off to bake a cake, and then there was one.

One little fairy, sitting all alone,
Decided to get married, and then there were none.

THE GIRL WHO LOVED ANIMALS

Once upon a time there was a girl called Willow, who loved all living creatures. There wasn't a single creature in the neighbourhood where she lived who hadn't at some time or another had cause to be grateful to Willow.

Whenever her father, who was a farmer, set out to cut his corn, Willow would first go into the field and gently remove all the little field mice nests from the stalks of corn and put the little creatures in a place of safety. Then she would warn all the rabbits and finally, when she was sure that the

field was completely empty, then and only then would she allow her father to cut the corn.

Once she sat up all night with a sparrow which had broken its wing, and quite often she would go hungry because she had given her food to some starving woodland creature.

Because of her great love for birds and animals, Willow soon learned their language and as she wandered through the countryside she often had a rabbit or two following her and perhaps a bird sitting on her shoulder. Willow would laugh and chatter away to these creatures as though they were boys and girls of her own age.

One hot summer's day Willow was sitting by the riverbank, talking to a little frog, but as she got up to go a little fish called from the water. "Please don't go, Willow. Your shadow on the water shields me from the sun."

"Then I'll stay little fish," replied Willow.

As the sun rose higher the little fish called out again. "Please lean out a little further, Willow, so that you can make more shade for my brothers and sisters."

Willow looked down and there, in the shady part of the river were dozens and dozens of little fish.

All day long the girl who loved animals stood by the riverbank, leaning forward with her arms outstretched to give as much shade as possible to the little fish. Then, as the sun was going down, she went home, promising to return again tomorrow.

Her parents began to worry about their daughter talking only to birds and animals and not making friends of her own, and so they decided it would be better for Willow if they sent her to live in the city for a while, with her aunt and uncle. There she would learn to meet and mix with other young people.

Willow was very sad when she heard of her parents' plan, but because she was a dutiful daughter she agreed to obey their wishes.

The next day, as she stood in her customary position on the riverbank, shading the little fish from the glare of the sun, she started to weep and her tears splashed down into the river, quite startling the little fish.

"Why are you so unhappy?" they asked.

Then Willow told them the whole sad story, how she must go to the city and stay with her aunt. "But who will look after you all while I am away?" she cried. "How I wish that I could stay here with you all forever."

A passing fairy heard this plea for help. "So you shall, my dear," she said, and gently touching the girl with her magic wand she turned her into a most beautiful and graceful tree . . . and ever since that day this tree has been known as a Weeping Willow.

So next time you're by a river and see a Weeping Willow tree stretching out to give shade to the little fish, think of the girl who loved animals. She's very happy now, for she knows she will never have to leave her friends.

Nursery Rhyme Objects

Each of the pictures on this page should remind you of a well-known nursery rhyme. Do you know all the rhymes?

ANSWERS

FIND THE NUMBER RHYMES

The answer to each of these questions is a number. If you don't know all the answers, you will find them among the nursery rhymes on the following pages.

1. How many mice did the farmer's wife chase?
2. How many blackbirds were baked in a pie?
3. How many fiddlers did Old King Cole have?
4. How many wigs did Gregory Griggs have?
5. How many kittens lost their mittens?
6. How many men had the brave old Duke of York?
7. How many mice sat down to spin?
8. How many wise men of Gotham were there?
9. How many Welshmen went hunting on St. David's Day?
10. How many tailors went out to catch a snail?

Three blind mice, see how they run!
They all ran after the farmer's wife,
Who cut off their tails with a carving knife,
Did you ever see such a thing in your life
As three blind mice?

Sing a song of sixpence,
A pocket full of rye;
Four and twenty blackbirds,
Baked in a pie.
When the pie was opened,
The birds began to sing;
Was not that a dainty dish,
To set before the king?

Old King Cole
Was a merry old soul,
And a merry old soul was he;
He called for his pipe,
And he called for his bowl,
And he called for his fiddlers three.

Gregory Griggs, Gregory Griggs,
Had twenty-seven different wigs.
He wore them up, he wore them down,
To please the people of the town.
He wore them east, he wore them west,
But he never could tell which he loved the best.

Three little kittens they lost their mittens,
And they began to cry,
"Oh, mother dear, we sadly fear
Our mittens we have lost."
"What! Lost your mittens, you naughty kittens!
Then you shall have no pie.
Mee-ow, mee-ow, mee-ow,
No, you shall have no pie."

Oh, the brave old Duke of York,
He had ten thousand men;
He marched them up to the top of the hill,
And he marched them down again.
And when they were up, they were up,
And when they were down, they were down,
And when they were only half way up,
They were neither up nor down.

Six little mice sat down to spin;
Pussy passed by and she peeped in.
"What are you doing, my little men?"
"Weaving coats for gentlemen."
"Shall I come in and cut off your threads?"
"No, no, Mistress Pussy, you'd bite off our heads."
"Oh, no, I'll not; I'll help you to spin."
"That may be so, but you don't come in."

Three wise men of Gotham,
They went to sea in a bowl,
And if the bowl had been stronger
My song would have been longer.

There were three jovial Welshmen,
As I have heard men say,
And they would go a-hunting
Upon St. David's Day.
All day they hunted
And nothing could they find,
But a ship a-sailing,
A-sailing with the wind.
One said it was a ship,
The other he said, Nay,
The third said it was a house,
With the chimney blown away.

Four and twenty tailors
Went to kill a snail,
The best man among them
Durst not touch her tail;
She put out her horns
Like a little Kyloe cow,
Run, tailors, run,
Or she'll kill you all e'en now.

Jack and Jill

THE STORY OF THE NURSERY RHYME

One day, as Jack and Jill came back from spending the afternoon with their friend Tom, the piper's son, who lived right at the other end of Nursery Rhyme Land, their mother met them at the gate of their cottage. In her hand she held a large pail, and she looked very cross.

"The old pump has run dry again," she said. "We really will have to have it mended when your father comes home from sea again. I'm afraid that you will have to go back up Steep Hill and bring me a pail of water from the well at the top."

"But mother, we have only just walked all the way from Tom's house," protested Jack, thinking of the long, steep climb up the hill.

"Can't it wait until after tea, mother?" asked Jill, who really was feeling very tired after her long walk.

"Not unless you both wish to go to Polly Flinders' party in dirty clothes," replied her mother firmly. "I need clean water to rinse your party dress, and you know how particular Mistress

Flinders is about people's dress. Look how angry she was when Polly ruined her dress by sitting too close to the cinders in the fireplace. Of course, I hardly blame the poor woman," she added, half to herself, "soot is very hard to get out."

"Oh, we'll go at once," replied Jill, who always liked to look her best at parties. "Come along, Jack. If we run we shall not be away too long."

"Slow down, Jill, this isn't a race," grumbled Jack, as he tried in vain to keep up with his sister. "It is only because you don't want Lucy Locket or Kitty Fisher to look prettier than you at the party tomorrow."

"Nonsense, I want to help mother," replied Jill, tossing her head. Then she added with a chuckle, "Besides, mother is the best seamstress in the whole of Nursery Rhyme Land, so my dress will be the prettiest."

"Oh, girls!" muttered Jack in disgust, and then he fell silent as he toiled up the hill. "Not far to go now," he said, as the well came in sight. "Goodness, Jill, look! There's naughty Johnny Green trying to drown their farm cat again. Last time Tommy Stout managed to rescue Topsy just in time. Hey, Johnny, leave that cat alone."

Hearing Jack's voice, Johnny let go of Topsy, who scampered away, back to the farm to hide in the barn.

"I was only giving Topsy a ride in the bucket," said Johnny, sulkily, as Jack and Jill reached the top of the hill.

"But it's dark down the well, and poor Topsy would be very frightened," protested Jill. "Don't play such a silly trick again, Johnny, or we shall tell your father. Topsy is a good mouser on the farm and I am sure that your father would hate to lose him."

"I'm sorry, I didn't think," muttered Johnny. "I won't do it again, I promise!"

Trying to make amends, Johnny helped Jack to fill their bucket of water. "Goodness, it *is* heavy," he cried. "I hope you get it home safely."

"Oh, we have carried much heavier buckets than this," replied Jack carelessly, beginning to show off just a

little. "Come on, Jill, let's run," he shouted, and quickened his pace.

But his sister was not expecting him to run, and was not holding the bucket very tightly at that moment. When Jack started to run, Jill let the handle go and Jack found himself stumbling down the hill, thrown off balance by the weight of the bucket.

A moment later he fell, and the water flew all over him. The bucket rolled away down the hill and Jack followed after it, meeting prickly gorse bushes and catching his hands and knees on stones as he rolled along.

"Jack, are you hurt?" called Jill anxiously, as Jack fell in a heap at the bottom of the hill. In her eagerness to reach Jack, Jill also stumbled and fell, but did not hurt herself.

"My head hurts," cried Jack sadly.

"Go to Dame Dob's cottage and tell her about your accident while Jill and I fill the bucket again and take it back to your mother," suggested Johnny Green. "Dame Dob has lots of herbs which she uses when people are ill. She made me a comfrey bandage when I sprained my ankle a few weeks ago."

"That's a splendid idea!" agreed

Jill warmly, and she helped her brother to the door of Dame Dob's cottage, before returning up the hill to help Johnny to carry the bucket.

"Dear, dear, Jack, what is wrong with your poor head?" asked Dame Dob kindly as Jack sank gratefully into a comfortable armchair. "That is a very nasty bruise on your head. Have you had a fall?"

"Yes, but it was my own silly fault. I was running down the hill," admitted Jack ruefully.

"Well, I'm sure that you won't do that again," said the old dame wisely as she busied herself with a large strip of brown paper and a big bottle of vinegar. "Stand close to the fire and your damp clothes will soon dry."

Jack watched as Dame Dob spread some ointment onto a cloth and then gently placed it over the bruise.

"That will soon make the bruise better," she said with a kind smile. "Does your head hurt too?" As Jack nodded, she added: "This is why I am going to bandage up your head with vinegar and brown paper. It makes a cool compress which will soon take your headache away."

"Thank you, Dame Dob, it feels better already," said Jack, as he felt the bandage beginning to cool his aching head. "Now I must go home in case my mother is worried."

"Remember not to run, and go straight to bed," warned Dame Dob. "Tomorrow you will be as right as rain."

Jill and his mother were anxiously awaiting his return, but when Jill saw the bandage on her brother's head she burst out laughing. "I'm sorry, Jack, but you really do look very funny with your head bandaged up with brown paper."

Jack looked rather hurt at Jill's words, and her mother scolded her soundly. "That was a very silly thing to say, Jill," she cried. "What does it matter how Jack looks, if the bandage eases his headache? Besides, a cold vinegar compress is well known as a remedy for an aching head. Jack should not have run down the hill, but you must not laugh at his misfortune."

"I'm sorry," said Jill, blushing a rosy-red. "I hope your head will soon be better, Jack."

"Oh, I'm sure that Jack will be quite well enough to go to school tomorrow," said his mother with a little smile.

And, of course, she was quite right. By next morning Jack's headache had completely gone and he and Jill went off to school as usual.

But when they reached the school, they discovered that Johnny had told all their friends about the previous day's escapade. Their friends formed a circle around Jack and Jill and sang merrily:

"Jack and Jill went up the hill
To fetch a pail of water;
Jack fell down and broke his
       crown,
And Jill came tumbling after."

DEEP AMONG THE CORAL CAVES

MERMAIDS AND MERMEN

Deep among the coral caves, at the bottom of the sea, live mermaids and mermen. These strange, but beautiful, creatures are half human and half fish.

The mermaids are very fond of mortal men and have often been seen sitting on a rock, combing their long, golden hair with a golden comb. If you looked very carefully, upon sighting a mermaid you would see that by her side she has a cap. This cap is endowed with magic powers, and when the mermaid sees the person of her choice she simply places the cap upon his head. He immediately becomes enchanted, and as long as he wears the magic cap he can live fathoms deep, at the bottom of the sea, without coming to any harm.

Mermen, too, are very fond of mortals and one will often marry a pretty girl and then take her down to live in his coral cave, which is decorated with a thousand different seashells.

LORELEI

The Lorelei is the name of a rock on the banks of the River Rhine in Germany. It is said that a wicked mermaid swam out of the sea and up the river, where she eventually came to rest on the Lorelei rock. Here she remained, combing her beautiful golden hair and singing the enchanting sea songs in her sweet voice, luring the boatmen too near the sharp, jagged rocks, and so to their death.

NEPTUNE – GOD OF THE SEAS

King Neptune controls all the waters of the earth and all the things within them. The mermaids and sea-serpents obey his every command and they all love and respect him for his wisdom. He is very large and strong, his hair and beard look like fresh sea foam and his eyes are the brightest periwinkle blue.

Each day he climbs into his beautiful chariot, made of shells and drawn by dolphins, and travels round his kingdom to see that all is well. In his hand he carries a spear, which looks very much like a toasting fork; this is called a trident and with it he can command the waters. It is just as well to keep King Neptune as happy as possible, for one wave of his trident can start an earthquake!

Tiny sea-urchins and gay sea-horses make up his court and with their mischievous tricks and bright, rainbow colours, it is not often that the King of all the Seas is sad.

SEA-SERPENTS

The sea was once full of these gigantic creatures, moving along the sea-bottom like giant lizards. They were usually green, scaly creatures, with quite small heads and huge bodies, ending in a very long tail. On warm, sunny days a sea-serpent might swim up from the sea-bed to bask in the warm sunlight, the white froth from the top of the waves making bubbly patterns on his back.

197

ROYAL RHYMES

Little girl, little girl, where have you been?
Gathering roses to give to the Queen.
Little girl, little girl, what gave she you?
She gave me a diamond as big as my shoe.

I had a little nut tree,
Yet nothing would it bear
But a silver nutmeg
And a golden pear.
The king of Spain's daughter
Came to visit me,
And all because of
My little nut tree.

Sing a song of sixpence,
A pocket full of rye;
Four-and-twenty blackbirds
Baked in a pie.
When the pie was opened,
The birds began to sing;
Wasn't that a dainty dish
To set before the king?

The king was in the counting-house,
Counting out his money;
The queen was in the parlour,
Eating bread and honey.
The maid was in the garden,
Hanging out the clothes;
When down came a little bird
And snapped off her nose.

Old King Cole was a merry old soul,
And a merry old soul was he;
He called for his pipe, he called for his bowl
And he called for his fiddlers three.

The Queen of Hearts
She made some tarts,
All on a summer's day.
The knave of Hearts
He stole those tarts,
And took them clean away.

The King of Hearts
Called for those tarts,
And beat the knave full sore.
The knave of Hearts
Brought back those tarts,
And vowed he'd steal no more.

When good King Arthur ruled this land,
    he was a goodly king,
He took three pecks of barley meal,
    to make a bag-pudding.
A bag-pudding the king did make,
    and stuffed it well with plums;
And in it put big lumps of fat,
    as big as my two thumbs.
The king and queen did eat thereof,
    and noblemen beside,
And what they could not eat that night,
    the queen next morning fried.

The Circus Trick

The bright sunshine shining in his face woke Pom-Pom, the French poodle.

He sneezed, shook himself, and went to the door to look outside. "What a lovely morning," he said to himself. "I'll go for a walk before breakfast."

Just outside the door a big bumble bee was playing leap-frog among the pansies. He would flutter his wings, leap over one flower and land on the next. He was such a heavy bee that the pansy petals sagged down as he landed, but he never fell off and quickly found the centre of the flower, where he gathered the nectar.

Pom-Pom watched the bee for a few minutes until he flew off and Pom-Pom couldn't see him any longer, even though he twisted his head this way and that.

So Pom-Pom ran down the garden and out into the lane and shouted a cheery 'good morning' to Tom, the next door cat, who was sitting by his gate, washing his paws and waiting for the milkman to come by.

Tom was quite a good friend, though Pom-Pom did sometimes chase him round the garden, just for fun, until Tom scrambled up the apple tree and laughed at Pom-Pom from the high branches.

Pom-Pom ran on until he came to the field where Mick, the white pony, lived. Mick was one of the ponies belonging to Mr. Brown's riding stables. All day he went up and down the lanes and through the little wood, carrying on his broad back the children who were learning to ride. Mick was very gentle and kind, and never fidgeted or kicked, and all the children loved him.

Before riding lessons started for the day he always went into the big field and had a good gallop round and a roll in the fresh green grass.

Pom-Pom pushed through a hole in the hedge and saw Mick racing across the field, the breeze making his long mane fly out behind him like a white scarf.

"Hello, Mick," called Pom-Pom. "Can I play with you?"

Mick galloped over and stopped in front of Pom-Pom, his big brown eyes shining with fun. "Come on then," he said to Pom-Pom. "I'll race you across the field."

The two friends got into line at the very edge of the field.

"One, two, three . . . go!" called Mick, and galloped off at a fast pace, with Pom-Pom beside him.

Before they were halfway to the opposite hedge, Mick was well ahead of Pom-Pom and the pony easily won the race.

"Oh dear," panted Pom-Pom, when he arrived at Mick's side, "you ought to give me a start, because your legs are much longer than mine!"

So they started again, and Mick allowed Pom-Pom to go quite a way down the field before he shouted "One, two, three . . . go!"

They were off again. This time it was much better. Mick and Pom-Pom

arrived at the opposite hedge exactly at the same time.

"A dead heat," called Mick. "You run very well, Pom-Pom."

The friends had two more races, then Mick, just to show how happy he was, jumped over the five-barred gate into the next field, his bright horseshoes flashing in the sun as he kicked his feet high to clear the top bar of the gate.

Pom-Pom took a leap and tried to jump between the second and third bar, but he stuck halfway through.

"Oh dear," he said, "I can't quite get through. Can you help me, Mick?"

So Mick jumped back over the gate again and gave Pom-Pom a push. Pom-Pom wriggled a bit and then, with a bump, he was through.

He shook himself, and the two friends laughed and lay down on the grass for a rest.

After a while, Pom-Pom said, "When the circus was in town last month, I saw a poodle called Frou-Frou riding round the ring on a pony's back. Do you think *we* could do that trick?"

"We can try it," said Mick. "You get on my back while I am lying down, and we'll see if you can balance."

So Pom-Pom climbed onto Mick's back, and Mick started to stand up. Pom-Pom's feet slipped a little and he rolled off onto the grass.

"Try again," said Mick.

Pom-Pom got up on the pony's back again and Mick carefully stood up.

"Hurrah!" shouted Pom-Pom. "We managed it. Now walk along slowly, Mick."

Mick began to walk. This was great fun.

"Go a little faster now," called Pom-Pom, and Mick trotted gently.

Pom-Pom felt very proud balancing there, while Mick went across the field.

Suddenly Pom-Pom and Mick heard the sound of clapping and, looking towards the gate, they saw several of the children from the riding stables watching them.

The children were clapping their hands with delight at Pom-Pom's trick. "You are clever," they called. "Please ride round again—it's just like the circus!"

The two friends rode round several times and Pom-Pom was so proud of himself that he forgot to balance carefully. His feet slipped, and he slid down Mick's back and landed on the grass.

Luckily he wasn't hurt, and the children ran into the field and made a great fuss of Mick and Pom-Pom and took them off to the stables for a great big breakfast.

"Well, I think it's time for the children's rides," said Mick. "Goodbye, Pom-Pom, we'll try the circus trick again another day."

"Goodbye, Mick," said Pom-Pom. "And thanks for the ride."

"What an interesting morning I've had," said Pom-Pom, as he trotted off home again.

AT THE MARKET

Young lambs to sell,
Young lambs to sell,
If I'd as much money as I can tell,
I never would cry young lambs to sell.

Rabbit, rabbit, rabbit pie!
Come, my ladies, come to buy;
Else your children they will cry.

Hot boiled beans, in very good butter,
Come, ladies and gentlemen, buy for your supper!

Cantaloupes! Cantaloupes! All very nice!
Eight for ten shillings, cheap at the price!

Hot-cross buns! Hot-cross buns!
One a penny, two a penny, hot-cross buns.
If you have no daughters, give them to your sons.
One a penny, two a penny, hot-cross buns!

The CROOKED MAN

THE STORY OF
THE NURSERY RHYME

Crispin Pennyfeather had been the royal coachman in Nursery Rhyme Land for as long as anyone could remember, but now his back was bent and his hands too stiff to hold the reins properly.

One day the King of Hearts came down to the royal stable where Crispin was trying to polish the harnesses, and spoke to him gently.

"Crispin, my dear old friend, I think the time has come for you to take a rest, for you have worked long and hard. So I have appointed a new coachman. He will, of course, live in the coach-house, and until I can find you a better house I am afraid you will have to make do with that old cottage near the old watermill. It is the only one left in Nursery Rhyme Land, but I have ordered the royal builders to build you a brand new house at once."

"Nay, Your Majesty, that old house will suit me fine," replied Crispin cheerfully. "I like its twisty chimneys and slanting windows. And if the thatch is a bit thin, well, a bit o' rain never hurt anyone badly, I reckon. When does the new coachman arrive?"

205

"Well, actually, he's in the kitchen now, taking a bite to eat," admitted the King. "But take your time moving, Crispin. My new coachman is Gregory Griggs, who has offered to stay with his friend Robert Barnes, the blacksmith, until his home is ready."

"He may move in today, Your Majesty," smiled Crispin. "It will not take me long to gather my few possessions together, and then I will be on my way."

"Let Gregory Griggs drive you in the royal coach," said the King, eager to help his old coachman in any way he could. "It is over a mile to the mill cottage and the lanes are very twisting and narrow so that it seems even longer."

"Nay, I still enjoy a good walk," replied Crispin with a smile. "The sky is blue, the sun is warm, and I have all the time in the world to get to the cottage. So I will bid you good-day, sire, and pray that Gregory serves you as faithfully as I did."

"He will never be a better coachman than you," replied the King. "Thank you, dear Crispin, for all your years of faithful service. You will be welcome at the palace whenever you wish to call. The Queen and I will always be pleased to see you."

"Thank you, Your Majesty," responded Crispin, his heart warmed by the king's kind words.

Soon he was walking out of the palace gates, his pack over his shoulder, whistling merrily. On the way to his new home he met several of his friends, and he stayed a few minutes to chat with them.

They were very surprised to hear his news, and as Crispin continued on his way Boy Blue and Jack Horner called a meeting of all the other nursery rhyme folk to tell them about an idea which they had both had.

Meanwhile, Crispin had stopped by the side of a stile for a rest on his journey. As he prepared to climb the stile a little later on, he saw something on the ground among the stubble.

"Why, it's a little crooked sixpence," he murmured to himself. "It must have been caught up by the reaper blades and squashed to this crooked shape. But I'm sure that it will still be good enough to spend."

He put it in his pocket and made his way through the cornfield. He could see the old watermill now, and knew that the end of his journey was in sight.

"I'm getting quite hungry too," he murmured aloud.

"Then stop a moment and share my lunch with me," said a merry voice, and there, smiling up kindly at Crispin from beneath the shade of a huge beech tree was Davy Delong, the little tinker with the sweet voice.

Davy was stirring a pot of mouth-watering stew, while nearby a thin little cat waited, hungrily, for his share.

From his pack Davy took out three dishes, and two wooden spoons, which he had carved himself, and filled the dishes with hot, tasty stew.

"Sit down, Crispin, and let us talk awhile. You know I am always ready for a chat," chuckled Davy as he handed the old coachman his stew. "Here, Catkin, here's some for you too," he called.

The cat rushed over eagerly to the dish which Davy set down on the grass, and began to eat hungrily.

"Your cat looks very hungry," said Crispin, as he watched the little creature eating his stew. "And he looks as if his leg has been injured at some time. The back one is quite crooked."

"He isn't really my cat," said Davy with a wry smile. "I bought him just now from a man who seemed to be treating him rather cruelly. He cost me sixpence. But I don't think that Catkin is really suited to my wandering kind of life. What he really needs is a good home and a kind master to look after him."

"Why, he is just what *I* need to keep me company," cried Crispin at once. "With my bent, crooked back, and his crooked back leg, we shall make a really comical pair, but I am sure we shall get on well together. Here, let me buy him from you for sixpence."

"Take him and welcome," replied Davy, smiling happily as he watched Catkin rub himself gently against Crispin, obviously very pleased with his new master. "But I want naught from you in return."

Then, suddenly, as he spied the shape of the coin that Crispin was holding out to him, he added eagerly: "Yes, I will take your sixpence, dear friend. Not in payment for Catkin, for I am only too glad that he has found a good home, but because a crooked sixpence is said to bring folk good luck."

After thanking Davy for the lunch, and washing the dishes in a nearby stream, Crispin set off again, this time with Catkin for company.

Suddenly Catkin pounced on a small harvest mouse which was fleeing to safety after its nest had been destroyed by the reapers.

"Nay, Catkin, the little creature has done us no harm. Let it go and he shall come and live with us also," said Crispin in a gentle voice.

"My name is Crookie," said the mouse to Catkin, who was now taking a kindly interest in his small companion. "My mother named me that because both my ears were crooked when I was born."

"Three crooked friends together," laughed Crispin. "But a cold welcome will await us at our cottage," he gently warned the animals. "It has been empty a long time and it has a leaking roof."

But a wonderful surprise awaited them when they finally arrived at the cottage. Smoke curled gaily from the twisty chimneys on the newly-thatched roof, the windows gleamed brightly, and everything was gay with paint.

Inside was a comfortable armchair near a blazing fire, the kettle was on the hob, and the table was filled with food. The room was packed with all Crispin's friends, who had planned this surprise when they had heard he was to move into the cottage.

"My cupboard may be empty, but yours certainly isn't," laughed Mother Hubbard, pointing to the well-stocked shelves. "And Mary's lamb and Bo-Peep's sheep have given you some lovely blankets and rugs to keep you warm."

"And we have brought you some broth," cried the children who lived in a shoe. "And Curly Locks has sent strawberries and cream, and Mrs. Horner one of her special plum pies."

"In fact, everyone has sent something or else come along themselves to help," explained Boy Blue. "We all wanted your new home to be as pleasant as possible."

"Then you must all stay to the house-warming," said Crispin as he sank gratefully into his armchair and told his friends everything that had happened that day.

Catkin and Crookie sat at either side of the fire, and after supper they were delighted to hear Tommy Tucker sing a new rhyme all about themselves. It went like this:

There was a crooked man,
Who walked a crooked mile,
He found a crooked sixpence,
Beside a crooked stile;
He bought a crooked cat,
Which caught a crooked mouse,
And they all lived together
In a little crooked house.

ONCE upon a time there were three Kings whose kingdoms were next to each other.

One summer, each King spent a week in each of the other two kingdoms.

At the end of their holiday King Arcon said: " Let us meet again in a year's time and see which of us has been able to make his kingdom the most beautiful."

" That is a splendid idea," cried King Fleurus.

" We will begin at once," agreed King Christian.

When the time for the meeting came each King looked proudly at his own city and felt sure there could not be a more beautiful sight.

The first city to be judged was that of King Arcon.

The three Kings and three Judges from a fourth kingdom set off on the tour.

King Arcon took them round the city himself.

" We will drive round every street in my city," he said, " and you will see that there is not one shabby nor ugly building left."

The Beautiful City

It was quite true. King Arcon had kept his subjects busy the whole year building beautiful halls, houses, and inns. The roads were clean and wide and the city shone with newly-cut stone. Not a broken-down building was to be seen.

" This is indeed a fine city," said one of the Judges.

" The Town Hall Square is a splendid sight," remarked the second.

But the third Judge looked at the people who stood or walked about the streets. People in shabby clothes because they were so poor. People with pale, tired faces, and children with thin little legs and solemn faces, who watched as the Kings rode by. People who were too tired or ill or unhappy to cheer their King as he passed.

The third Judge spoke in a low tone to the other two. Looking from the wonderful buildings to the people who built them they nodded and talked earnestly together.

The next day the two Kings and the three Judges met King Fleurus to be taken round his city.

King Fleurus had decided that his city should be made beautiful by flowers and trees.

As the three Kings and three Judges drove round the city really was a wonderful sight.

Every road was lined by a trim green verge. Flowering bushes and trees made splashes of colour, and beautiful hedges took the place of fences and walls.

In one part the hedges and bushes had been trimmed to the shape of animals and birds.

In the open squares of the city were beautiful flower beds full of the most wonderful blooms. There was not a corner

of the city that had not been beautified in this way. All the waste ground had become gardens—large or small.

Flowers in hundreds and thousands met the visitors' eyes as they drove round.

The Judges were loud in their praise of this beauty but, remembering the last city, they looked carefully at the people.

Here again they were disappointed. For the people did not match the beautiful city.

They looked sad and careworn. Many cripples were to be seen and all were dressed in dull and shabby clothes. The children were no better than those in King Arcon's city. Most of them had pale thin faces. They were ill fed and often in rags.

" The children should look like flowers, too," murmured one Judge to another.

However nothing was said to the Kings as there was still the third city to visit.

The following day they met in King Christian's city.

No sooner had the Kings' coach set off, followed by the three Judges in an equally splendid coach, than the streets became lined with people. Clapping and laughing they cheered their King as he passed.

The Judges looked at each other, and then at the people again.

What a difference! Everyone was dressed in bright gay colours, and their faces were full of joy. All seemed to be strong and healthy, with rosy faces and straight and sturdy limbs. But the children were the best sight of all.

"These children *are* like flowers," said one Judge to another, and indeed they were.

Standing at the roadside in little groups as they had come out of their schools were boys and girls of all ages. All wore the prettiest clothes you could imagine, in dozens of different colours. Their faces were bright and smiling as they waved flags or threw flowers to their King. Their voices were strong and sweet when they sang to him as he passed.

Nobody noticed if every building was perfect or if all the waste ground had been tidied up, for the three Judges could not take their eyes off the children.

Never had they seen such a gay and happy crowd!

At last the tour was over, and the three Kings and three Judges met in King Christian's palace.

King Arcon and King Fleurus were very quiet. What they had just seen had astonished them.

At last one of the Judges spoke. "I think King Christian's city is the most beautiful I have ever seen," he said.

"Yes," agreed the second. "The buildings and gardens of the other two are indeed a wonderful sight, but such happiness as we have just seen is better far than those."

"I agree without a doubt," nodded the third Judge. "For, after all, people are of

213

more importance than buildings or gardens."

King Arcon and King Fleurus waited no longer. They both stepped forward and laid a hand on the shoulder of King Christian.

"My friend," said King Arcon, "I see now that what you have done is the only way to beautify a city, for with the people healthy and happy everything is possible."

"And I," said King Fleurus, "can only beg that you will tell us how you set to work to bring about such a miracle."

King Christian smiled. "It will be a pleasure," he said, "and now let us go to the banqueting hall."

So the three Kings and the three Judges dined together.

They listened to all King Christian had to tell them and went away full of plans and hopes for the future.

As for King Christian, he felt happier than ever to think that in time there would be many other cities as beautiful as his own.

INDOOR SNOWMAN

No need to wait for the snowy weather or to go outside to make your snowman this year! This jolly fellow can be made inside, sitting by the fire, and he will decorate your home throughout the festive season without even melting!

MATERIALS:

Two pieces of small mesh chicken wire; packet of white tissue paper; scraps of stiff black paper; scraps of stiff red paper; strip of red crepe paper or red cloth; glue; piece of string.

TO MAKE SNOWMAN:

Shape the pieces of chicken wire into two round balls; one standing about 3 inches high, the other about 2 inches high. Place the smaller ball on top of the larger one and tie securely in place with a piece of string, threading it through the wire loops.

From the tissue paper cut 4 inch squares. Tuck one square into each hole of the wire mesh, pushing the centre of the square into the hole with your finger. Fill head and body, leaving base of body empty so that snowman can stand up.

Cut six small circles from stiff black paper. Glue three on centre front of body to make buttons. Glue other three in place on head to make eyes and nose. From red paper cut curved strip for mouth and glue in place. Tie strip of red crepe paper or old red cloth round neck to make scarf.

TO MAKE SNOWMAN'S HAT:

On black paper draw, preferably with a compass, two circles: one with a radius of $1\frac{1}{4}$ inches and one with a radius of $\frac{3}{4}$ inch. Draw, also on the black paper, an oblong measuring 2 inch by $4\frac{3}{4}$ inch. Cut out the three shapes.

Bring the 2 inch. ends of oblong together to form a tube and glue ends. Glue smaller circle on top of tube to make top of hat, and glue larger circle on bottom of tube to make base and rim of hat.

Cut thin strip of red paper to make hat band and glue in place. Glue hat to snowman's head.

JOHNNIE'S RIVER CRUISE

Johnnie Rabbit looked down from High Rock, on the moor where he lived, down over the wood, down to the rabbit burrows by the river. It was a long time since he had seen his brother Bob and he set off to pay him a call.

It was a fine morning and soon he was well on his way. The wood was very quiet. There was nobody about at all; just the birds waking and whistling their morning songs, one by one, until at last they all sang together in a fine dawn chorus.

On the ground he smelt Fox. But he kept a careful lookout and saw no sign of movement. All the animals which hunted in the night seemed to have fed and returned to their homes to sleep the daylight hours away.

The sun came up, and on the river bank, as he drew near, he could see the rabbit colony feeding outside their burrows, and among them was his brother Bob.

Nearby were several small rabbits, all very much like Bob, and Johnnie was very pleased to see them, for he knew they must be Bob's family.

Suddenly all the rabbits turned and bolted and Johnnie Rabbit sat very still and watched, and waited.

For some time nothing happened and then—yes, there it was—a movement among the reeds, a something which crept a little nearer to the one solitary baby rabbit which did not seem to know it had been left alone. Johnnie knew who it was, there in the rushes. It was Rennie Fox, seeking a late breakfast.

"Ha," said Johnnie Rabbit to himself, "but he's not going to have my brother Bob's baby bunny for breakfast." And then, before he could think any more, he sneezed, "*Atishoooo!*" for a grass stalk had tickled his nose.

Rennie Fox swung round and glared at him, then licked his chops with a very red tongue.

"Ha! Ha!" said Rennie Fox. "Here's a much bigger breakfast than a baby bunny!" And he leapt forward, very near to Johnnie Rabbit—but not quite near enough.

Then the chase began, Rennie Fox determined to have Johnnie for breakfast and Johnnie determined that he shouldn't! Several times Rennie Fox's jaws snapped with a loud SNAP-SNAP, very close indeed!

They dodged and they ran so fast that neither had time to look around, neither had time to see Bobbie Rabbit come back for his baby bunny, neither had time to see something else! The river had risen quickly, and soon, when they swung round, they both found themselves running in the edge of the water. *Ugh!* Neither of them liked to get their paws so wet as that!

SNAP-SNAP! SNAP-SNAP! That was far too near. Johnnie felt a small piece of fur pulled away in Rennie's teeth.

He was getting out of breath when he saw a chance too good to be missed. Down the river was floating a tree trunk, and he jumped and landed safely as it floated by. It was only a small birch tree, strong enough to carry his weight—but not strong enough for Rennie Fox, who jumped after him and slid down off the log into the water.

"Oh! Oh! Oh! Oh!" spluttered Rennie Fox. "Help me up. I'm drowning!"

"No fear!" panted Johnnie, who knew perfectly well that Rennie could swim. "Not on my log. You don't come here, you don't. Back to the bank with you!"

But Rennie hadn't finished yet. The log floated away down the river and always, among the trees on the bank side, Johnnie could see the red form of Rennie Fox following, waiting for the log to come near enough. Johnnie shivered and watched carefully.

When the river bend came, the current swung his log near to an overhanging branch. Rennie Fox had to go round the high wall and didn't see him jump off the log into the tree. But by the time Johnnie had climbed through the branches and was ready to jump down to the ground, Rennie Fox was back, sitting there, grinning and snapping, waiting patiently. Johnnie was trapped.

The sun was getting higher in the sky when: "*Wha-hooooo!*"

The sound came from up the wood. Johnnie knew what it was, and so did Rennie Fox. He barked, delightedly. It was a she-fox looking for a mate. Presently she came down the wood, and Johnnie watched with excitement, for close beside her was a third fox.

Rennie Fox took one look at him and then forgot all about Johnnie Rabbit and breakfast. Next moment there was a flurry of fur as the two dog-foxes fought and the she-fox sat watching with interest to see who would win.

But Johnnie didn't stop to see. He jumped from the tree and ran—high up the hillside, far away from the river and the foxes, away up to the moor. It was a long way but he didn't stop till he sat once more on High Rock and looked down, down to the river side far below where two red foxes trotted side by side towards the wood, and a third one limped home all by himself.

And Johnnie smiled. "Poor Rennie!" he said to himself. "He didn't get any breakfast, but he *has* won a mate. I'm glad he didn't get me for breakfast. That I am!"

RHYMING RIDDLES

In marble halls as white as milk,
Lined with a skin as soft as silk,
Within a fountain crystal clear,
A golden apple doth appear.
No doors there are to this stronghold,
Yet thieves break in and steal the gold.

What is it?

Riddle me, riddle me ree,
A little man in a tree;
A stick in his hand,
A stone in his throat,
If you answer this riddle
I'll give you a groat.

What is it?

Hickamore, hackamore,
On the king's kitchen door,
All the king's horses,
And all the king's men,
Could not drive hickamore hackamore,
Off the king's kitchen door.

What was it?

As I went over London Bridge,
I met Mr. Rusticap;
Pins and needles on his back
A-going to Thorney Fair.

Who was he?

I have a little sister,
Folk call her Peep, Peep,
She wades in the water,
Deep, deep, deep;
She climbs up the mountains;
High, high, high,
But my poor little sister
Has only got one eye.

What is she?

Daffy-down-dilly
Is new come to town,
In a yellow petticoat,
And a green gown.

Who is she?

I'm called by the name of a man,
Yet am as little as a mouse;
When winter comes I love to be
Within my red target near my house.

Who am I?

ANSWERS:
AN EGG; A CHERRY; A SUNBEAM;
A HEDGEHOG; A STAR;
A DAFFODIL; A ROBIN REDBREAST.

A JUMBO APPETITE

Do you like elephants? If you've ever thought that you'd like to own one, you'd be surprised to learn how much food an elephant eats in one day.

He eats a quarter of a ton of hay or grass each day.

He drinks 50 gallons of water each day.

It takes 12 zoo keepers to carry his food each day.

It takes 10 zoo keepers carrying buckets holding 5 gallons of water to carry his water each day.

The Little Red Ball

The little red ball was feeling squashed and uncomfortable. He was right at the bottom of the toybox, and all the other toys had been thrown in on top of him. There was a large tin soldier sticking in his side, and a very heavy fire-engine squashing him on the top.

"Oh, I wish I had a comfortable home," cried the little red ball. "How I wish Jimmy would look after me properly!"

All the toys belonged to a little boy called Jimmy. But he had so many that he never took care of them, or even played with them often.

One day, Jimmy's cousin, Colin, came to stay, and he wanted to see all the toys. Some of them hadn't been played with for weeks, but now out they all came.

"Gosh, you *are* lucky having all these toys," said Colin, as he marched the toy soldier up and down.

The little red ball listened anxiously. He was desperately hoping that Colin would want to play with him.

After Colin and Jimmy had tired of playing with the soldier, Colin noticed the little red ball.

"Come on, Jimmy!" he yelled. "Let's play football in the garden." And, to the little red ball's delight, he was picked up and carried out into the garden.

The boys had great fun kicking the ball to each other, and how happy the little red ball was to be played with again. But then Jimmy kicked it too hard, and over the fence at the bottom of the garden sailed the little red ball.

"Gosh, what a kick!" cried Colin. "But we'd better go and find it now."

"Oh, why bother," said Jimmy. "I've got lots of other toys to play with." And they went indoors.

The little red ball had landed in the middle of some bushes, and he began to wonder what would happen to him now. He was left there all night, but in the morning he had some visitors.

First, a small brown bird came hopping along, looking for worms. He stopped, cocked his head on one side, and stared at the little ball.

"Who are you?" he cheeped. "Are *you* looking for worms, too?"

The little red ball answered sadly that he was waiting for someone to find him, and he asked the little bird if he wanted a ball.

"A ball!" he cheeped. "What would I do with a ball? Haven't got time to play. Too busy looking for food." And off he flew.

Soon along came the cat from down the road.

"*Miaow,* hello," she purred. "Haven't seen you before. Are you new around here?"

The little red ball wasn't sure whether he was new or not, but he asked the cat if she'd like to play with him.

"Oh no, thank you," she said, stretching herself lazily. "I might get my lovely fur dirty, playing in these bushes, and then I'd have to wash it again, wouldn't I?" And off she sauntered.

The next visitor came bounding noisily up to the little red ball and sniffed at it. It was the puppy who lived in the house.

"*Woof!*" he barked. "What are you doing in my garden? Do you belong to David?"

"Who's David?" asked the little

red ball curiously.

"He lives in the house. I belong to him," said the puppy, playfully giving the little red ball a few cuffs with his paw.

The little red ball told the puppy where he'd come from, and asked him if he wanted to play with him.

"That might be fun," barked the puppy, and he started nosing the ball along the ground and patting it with his paw.

At last I've got someone to play with, thought the little red ball. But then a voice from the house called out, "Benjy!"

"That's me!" barked the puppy, explaining that it was his dinner-time. And off he scampered.

Once more the little red ball was left alone, this time in the middle of the lawn.

Sometime later, David, the little boy who lived in the house, came out into the garden and noticed the little red ball lying there.

"Mummy, Mummy," he called excitedly. "Look what I have found!" And he picked up the ball and ran indoors.

David hadn't got many toys, and he was so pleased with the little red ball. David's Mummy washed the ball in a big bowl of soapy water till it shone like new. How happy the little red ball was; he knew he would be properly looked after now.

David played with him often, and they had great fun together. He even had his own special place on the toy-shelf, all to himself, which made him very pleased indeed!

KING of the JUNGLE

The lion, who has been called the King of the beasts, is a magnificent animal. He is a member of the big cat family, which includes pumas, cheetahs, leopards and tigers.

Most wild lions today are found in Africa. The lion's tawny coat matches the sunny open plains on which he lives. He can climb trees very well and often sits on a branch for hours at a time, especially after he has eaten a tasty meal.

A lion's home is called a den or lair and his wife is called a lioness. She looks after their lion cubs, which are called whelps. The cubs are born with spots on their thick woolly fur but these soon disappear.

Lions have a fine mane and a strange brush of long hair at the end of their tails called a 'claw' or 'thorn'.

The kings of ancient Egypt, who were called Pharaohs, used to keep lions as their pets and allow them to roam freely around the court.

QUESTION TIME

How much have you remembered about what you have just read? Try and answer these questions, and if you can't do this, find the answers from the text.

Where do most lions live?

What is a lion's home called?
Can lions climb trees?
Who kept lions as pets?
What are baby lions called?
To what family do lions belong?
Do lion cubs have spots?
Can you name two other animals belonging to the cat family?

NURSERY RHYME PICTURES

Can you complete this well-known nursery rhyme by putting the correct picture in the blank spaces?

There was a crooked ——————,

Who walked a crooked ——————,

And he found a crooked ——————,

Beside a crooked ——————,

He bought a crooked ——————,

Which caught a crooked ——————,

And they all lived together

In a little crooked ——————

CONTRARY MISTRESS MARY

THE STORY OF THE NURSERY RHYME

"I really don't know what is the matter with Mistress Mary these days," sighed Mr. Bunn, the baker, to Mother Hubbard when she came into his shop in Nursery Rhyme Land to buy some cakes. "Yesterday she asked me specially to make a large, iced cake with her name on it, and when I delivered it to her she said that she had changed her mind and did not want it after all. If I had not seen the other Mary, with her little lamb, who bought it instead, I should have wasted both my time and my ingredients."

"Oh, dear, you are yet another complaining about Mistress Mary," replied Mother Hubbard, shaking her head sadly. "She is beginning to lose all her friends because of her contrariness. Do you remember the party we went to at the crooked man's cottage?"

"I do indeed," smiled Mr. Bunn. "We all had a really lovely time."

"Well, everyone did except Mistress Mary," went on Mother Hubbard. "Instead of sympathising with Lucy Locket over the loss of her pocket, Mary told her it served her right for

being so careless, and she upset Jack Horner by saying that his mother's plum pie needed more sugar."

"I wish she would mend her ways," said Mr. Bunn. "Nursery Rhyme Land is usually such a happy place. I hate to see Mary upsetting everyone like this."

"Perhaps something will happen to make her more like her old self," said Mother Hubbard as she hurried off to the butcher's shop to get a bone for her dog.

But the days passed and Mistress Mary seemed to get even more and more contrary. Asked to tea by Polly and Sukey she never arrived, after promising to come early to help make the tea. She laughed when Bo-Peep lost her sheep, and she passed Boy Blue sleeping under a haystack and refused to tell the farmer where to look for him – all out of sheer contrariness!

Then, one day, the King of Hearts sent his royal herald all round his kingdom telling the people that on a certain day soon the Princess of Sugar Plum Land was coming to visit Nursery Rhyme Land.

"His Majesty asks, most politely, that everyone does all they can to make the Princess Sugar Almond's visit a happy one!" called out the herald.

"I know one way we can please the Princess," said Jack Horner. "She loves gardens and flowers, and since here in Nursery Rhyme Land we can grow any flower in any season let's all make pretty gardens for the Princess to see as she passes by in the royal carriage."

"What a splendid idea!" cried everyone, and they set to work at once.

Lawns were cut and hedges trimmed, and beautiful enchanted flowers were planted, which sprang up overnight. Soon every garden was a riot of colour and everyone felt very pleased.

"The princess will think that she is visiting Flower Land, not Nursery Rhyme Land," laughed Miss Muffet, as she looked admiringly at the tall hollyhocks and other bright, garden flowers which filled the tiny wayside cottage where Mrs. Horner lived with her son, Jack.

"Not if she enters the kingdom from the south," retorted Jack Horner, rushing up to Molly Muffet. "I have just been round to see everyone's garden. They are all lovely . . . except for the one belonging to Contrary Mary. Honestly, Molly, it is a sheer disgrace! There are weeds everywhere, and Mistress Mary's garden will be the first one the princess will see as she drives along. She might be so disgusted that she could cancel her visit altogether."

"Did you ask Mistress Mary why her garden was so untidy?" asked Molly, looking very upset. "Surely she heard the herald announce the princess's visit?"

"Of course she did!" replied Jack. "But, being contrary as usual, she decided that since others were making their gardens pretty, her own garden could stay the ugliest of all. Why, I even offered to tidy up the garden myself, but Mistress Mary merely tossed her head and ordered me not to do so."

"I wonder why Mary is so bad-tempered?" said Molly, thoughtfully. "I'm sure that there is a particular reason. If only we could discover what it is, then perhaps we could do something about it."

"We haven't got much time," responded Jack, glumly. "The royal visit starts tomorrow."

The two friends thought hard about contrary Mistress Mary for a long time. Then Molly cried suddenly: "Jack, Mary started being contrary the day Lucy Locket lost her pocket.

Kitty Fisher found it later and returned it to Lucy, and since then the two girls have been firm friends. But Kitty was always Mary's special friend and I believe she is jealous. Look, here come Kitty and Lucy now. I shall tell them that I think I know why Mary has turned so horrid."

"Oh, silly Mary, we could all be friends!" cried Kitty as Molly Muffet told her the whole story. "Come along, Lucy, we will go now to see Mary and try and make her be more sensible."

Mistress Mary was rather haughty with Lucy and Kitty when they first arrived, but when Lucy shyly admitted how greatly she admired Mary because she never misplaced or lost anything, and Kitty hugged her hard and told her that she was just as fond of Mary as ever, Mistress Mary admitted to being a silly little goose and promised to mend her ways.

"Well, first you must get this garden tidy. Come along, Lucy and I will help you," said Kitty firmly.

Soon all the weeds had disappeared and, due to a very special magic spell brought by Kitty, the enchanted flowers bloomed at once.

"There, now your garden looks as pretty as the others," said Kitty as she finished filling the small pool in Mary's garden with fresh water, much to the delight of the goldfish who lived there.

Mary looked at her garden for a moment. Then, with a little secret smile, she went indoors. She returned a few moments later with some delicate silver wind bells which she hung on the old apple tree so that they tinkled in the breeze.

Then she handed her two friends each a bag, and asked them to decorate the garden border with the pretty cockle shells they would find in the bags.

"Now my garden is really finished," she said, as her two friends stood by her side, admiring their handiwork.

Just at that moment Jack Horner came by and, with a huge grin, he asked cheekily:

"Mistress Mary, quite contrary,
How does your garden grow?"

The three friends, all standing neatly in a row, answered together with a chuckle:

"With silver bells and cockle shells
And pretty maids all in a row."

When the princess passed by next day she said Mary's garden was the prettiest and the most unusual one she had ever seen, and from that day Mary was no longer contrary, and her *two* best friends were Kitty Fisher and Lucy Locket.

FAIRY FRIENDS

Did you know that many of the fairy folk have their own very special friends among the animals and birds which make their homes in the woodland glades where the fairies live?

THE BAKER'S FRIEND

When Bushytail Squirrel wakes up in the springtime he never needs to go searching for the nuts which he collected the previous autumn before going to sleep for the winter. He knows that they are all safely stored away in the loft of Honeypot Cottage, the home of Sugar and Spice, the fairy bakers.

Bushytail once came to the baker's rescue when they had no nuts to decorate a very special cake ordered by the Fairy Queen for the visit of Duke Marzipan Walnut to Fairyland. Bushytail generously gave Sugar all his best nuts, and the cake was such a great success that Sugar and Spice were allowed to put the words ROYAL BAKERS after their names on the sign which hangs outside their little shop.

They were so pleased about this that they offered to store Bushytail's nuts for him, an offer which the little squirrel accepted eagerly, and the three of them have been firm friends ever since.

SWIFTSHOES' FRIEND

Swiftshoes is the elfin messenger who takes messages all over Grassy Glade, at all hours of the day and night. Because he cannot fly like the fairies, the Fairy Queen gave him a special pair of magic shoes which allow Swiftshoes to travel ten times as fast as anyone else.

Swiftshoes enjoyed his work, but at night the glade often seemed rather a strange and frightening place when everyone was asleep. The little elf often longed for company and someone to talk to, on his journeys through the night.

Then, one very dark night, when the moon was hidden behind the clouds playing hide-and-seek with the stars, Swiftshoes was asked to take a very urgent message to Dame Dimple, who lived right at the edge of Grassy Glade,

almost in Daffodil Dale. Her old friend, Dame Dapple, was ill and the old lady asked Swiftshoes to go and ask Dame Dimple to come at once to look after her and her pet dog, Puck, and her cat, Twinkle.

Swiftshoes agreed to go very willingly, for he was very fond of Dame Dapple, who always found him a piece of gingerbread to eat before he set off on any journey for her. But as he caught his foot in a rabbit hole for the third time, he sighed deeply and thought longingly of his cosy little bed in Sleepy Hollow.

Suddenly he heard the sound of wings above his head, and a soft voice called: "Hello, Swiftshoes, it's a dark night for walking alone. May I give you a lift?" Swiftshoes found himself looking up at Brighteyes the owl. "I have often thought that you might like a ride at night," went on Brighteyes shyly, "and to-night is very dark indeed."

"Oh, thank you," murmured the little elf as he climbed up onto the owl's back. "This is kind of you, Brighteyes," and he told him where to go.

Chatting happily together, they soon reached Dame Dimple's Cottage, for Brighteyes could see very well in the dark and his strong wings flew very swiftly. Dame Dimple promised to go to see her friend as soon as the first rays of dawn appeared in the sky.

As they flew back to tell Dame Dapple, they resolved that each time Swiftshoes had to make a journey by night he should go on the back of Brighteyes.

So, if you are ever walking through Grassy Glade on a moonlight night and see a large owl flying through the trees with a small elf perched on his back, you will know that it is Brighteyes and Swiftshoes delivering an important message.

THE GARDENER'S FRIEND

At least three times a week you can see Rosie Rabbit pulling along a cart, piled high with fruit and vegetables, and driven by Greenfingers, the fairy gardener.

Greenfingers used to offer his wares for sale from his wheelbarrow, which was very heavy to push. One day the wheel hit a large stone and all the produce tumbled out.

Rosie, who lived in a nearby burrow, saw the accident and rushed out to help Greenfingers pick everything up.

"I am sure you must get very tired pushing that wheelbarrow," said Rosie. "If you get Nimblefingers, the fairy carpenter, to make you a cart, I will pull it along for you."

"What a splendid idea," cried Greenfingers in delight. "And in return I will supply enough lettuce leaves and carrots to feed your entire family."

This arrangement worked very well and Greenfingers sold more fruit and vegetables than ever before because now he could travel as far as Daffodil Dale and Buttercup Meadow with his rabbit cart.

PERKIN THE PEDLAR'S FRIEND

Another person in Grassy Glade who was selling more wares was Perkin, the pixie pedlar, because of the help he received from his great friend Tiny, the fieldmouse. It was Tiny's task each day to collect all the small objects left in Grassy Glade by picnickers, and the little fieldmouse gave Perkin everything he collected. Tiny liked Perkin because he was never too busy to chat and he had once rescued Tiny from drowning in Pixie Pond.

Perkin sold these on his tray in the pixie market and a lost lace handkerchief made a fine tablecloth for Fairy Amethyst, who also bought a silver thimble as a hat for her friend Goblin Garnet; while a lost silver button made a beautiful plate for Nimble Gnome.

LARRY'S MAGIC STICK

There was once a kind-hearted boy named Larry who lived with his Granny in a little tumbledown cottage at the end of a winding green lane.

The roof of the cottage leaked, and on rainy days water trickled into the bedroom and lay on the floor in pools. It was not surprising that the old woman became quite ill with rheumatism.

"Oh dear, oh dear, what shall we do?" she said one morning after it had rained in torrents all night and the bedroom was littered with pails and bowls in which to catch the water.

Then she hobbled to a queer little dark cupboard in a corner of the kitchen and drew out an old shiny teapot. "See, there are only a few silver coins left! We shall soon be quite penniless!" she said as she took off the lid and held it out so that Larry could see how her small savings had dwindled.

"Cheer up, Granny! I will go this very day to get work and earn a little money. You shall have the roof mended before long, never fear!" said Larry, as he wrapped up some bread and cheese in a clean red handkerchief. Then, stuffing it into his pocket, he kissed his Granny and set off down the lane, whistling a jolly tune.

As he strode along the path by the side of the river Larry suddenly heard a cry for help, and there in the middle of the stream, struggling wildly, was a strange little man.

In the twinkling of an eye Larry threw down his coat and leaped into the water. How cold it was! But he swam out bravely, took hold of the little man, and carried him safely to the bank.

"Thank you, my good fellow!" said the stranger, as he lay in the grass, gasping for breath. "You have saved my life."

When he had recovered a little he led Larry to his hut in the forest, where they dried their clothes before a fire of blazing logs.

"And now," said the queer little man, "I must reward you for your kind action!" And, leading Larry into the green glade behind the hut, he broke off a twig from a twisted crab-apple tree.

"This is an enchanted tree!" he said. "You have only to make a wish as you tap this twig on the ground three times, and you will be surprised how quickly the wish will come true."

Larry was just going to thank the queer little man when he vanished

236

from sight in a puff of green smoke. So he put the funny magic twig in his pocket and trudged off through the forest.

As he climbed a stile and began to cross a field, suddenly up from the ground sprang the little man. "I forgot to tell you," said he, "the magic twig will only give you three wishes, and I'm afraid you must not wish for anything for yourself or your family."

And so saying, he sprang into a tree and disappeared down the inside of the trunk.

"Well, I am not so lucky as I thought!" said Larry to himself. "I shall not be able to wish for a nice new cottage, and a box of gold, and a smart little pony-cart for Granny and me. I don't think the magic twig is of any use at all!"

"Oh, yes, it is!" cried a small squeaky voice. And turning round Larry was astonished to see a fluffy brown squirrel sitting on the forest fence.

"I could not help hearing what the Old Man of the Wood told you," said the tiny creature, looking at Larry with his bright brown eyes, "and your magic twig could do the squirrels in this wood a great service."

"I should be glad to help you," replied Larry.

So the little creature leaped upon his shoulder and said: "We want to get rid of Rusty the fox. He scratches under every tree and spoils all our store cupboards. We have begged him to leave them alone, but he only laughs and makes fun of us. We are afraid we shall never get enough stores for winter if old Rusty is not cured of his tricks."

"Leave it to me," said Larry with a laugh. Then he took out his funny magic twig, and tapped it upon the ground, saying:

Tick, tack, tick!
Catch the red fox, quick, quick, quick,
Take him by his bushy tail,
And send him over hill and dale!"

At once the magic twig twisted and turned and flew off into the wood. In no time at all Larry heard the bark of Rusty the fox, as the magic twig beat

him until he cried for mercy. When the twig came back into its master's hand, the fox was running over hill and dale as fast as his legs would carry him.

The squirrel was so pleased to see the end of the fox that he ran off to his treehouse, and in a flash he returned with a shining golden acorn. This he gave to Larry before he set off again on his travels.

Larry soon came to a busy town, and there he met an old woman trudging home from market with a heavy load of bread and vegetables.

"Please help me with my baskets," she asked, as she almost fainted with weariness.

"I will do more than that," said

Larry, taking out the little magic twig. And he tapped it on the ground three times, saying:

"Tick, tack, tick!
Little magic stick,
Send a donkey cart I pray,
To help the old dame on her way!"

In the twinkling of an eye the astonished old lady beheld a sturdy little grey donkey and a gay red cart. She could hardly believe her eyes. But Larry helped her up into the cart, and handed her the baskets and bags. Then he jumped in the cart himself, and taking hold of the reins, drove her all the way to her little house in a leafy lane.

The old lady was so delighted with her new possessions that she gave Larry a pretty little musical box. It had a tiny dancing lady on the lid, and every time a little knob was turned the tinkling music could be heard, and the little dancer spun round and round.

After thanking the old woman, Larry set off once again. He came at last to a great castle set on a high hill. There he found all the servants running backwards and forwards across the courtyard, carrying golden plates and dishes heaped high with delicious food.

"It is the Princess's birthday!" said a little pantry-boy whom Larry stopped by the kitchen door.

"I should like to give her three gifts," said Larry.

The servants who heard him began to laugh. "What can a poor boy like you give to a beautiful Princess?" they said.

But Larry ran up to the soldiers who guarded the great studded door of the castle and asked them if he might see the Princess.

"Indeed not!" they roared, looking haughtily at Larry in his old patched clothes.

At that moment the doors swung open and the rich Duke came out, followed by six servants. He looked kindly at Larry. "Yes, you may give

your gifts to my daughter, the Princess!" he said.

So Larry was taken into a fine room furnished with golden chairs, deep couches covered with silk and satin, and thick carpets into which his feet sank as if he walked on a cloud.

The Duke and the Princess thought that Larry would give a bouquet of woodland flowers. How surprised they were when he asked the Princess to wish for anything she desired in the world.

"I would like a golden ship that would sail on water, fly through the air, and travel swiftly and smoothly on land," said the Princess, laughing.

Larry took out his little magic twig, tapped it three times on the ground, and said:

"Tick, tack, tick!
Little magic stick!
Send a golden vessel fair,
To sail the sea, to float through air,
Or travel smoothly anywhere!"

At once the enchanted ship stood before them. The Duke and the Princess, and the courtiers and the servants gasped in astonishment. They were so delighted that Larry was given a splendid new suit of clothes, a white horse, a golden coach and ten bags of gold. And though they begged him to stay at the castle and take part in the Princess's birthday celebrations he said he must leave at once, as he had important work to do.

Larry was so pleased with his good fortune that he quite forgot to give the Princess the golden acorn and the old lady's musical box.

But his Granny was glad to have them. The golden acorn is kept to this day in her old shiny teapot. And the musical box stands on the mantelpiece of her fine new cottage which Larry had bought with some of his gold.